Obstetrics and Gynaecology

DNB Topic-wise Question Bank

Updated with the Latest Question Paper

4th Edition

Obstetrics and Gynaecology

DNB Topic-wise Question Bank

Updated with the Latest Question Paper

4th Edition

Mythri Sharan BK
MBBS, DGO (Manipal), DNB
Fellowship in Cosmetic Gynaecology, Dubai
Consultant, Apollo Cradle, Hyderabad

PMB

PARAS Medical Books Pvt. Ltd.

Hyderabad (HO) • Ameerpet (Hyd) • Bangalore • Delhi
Hyderguda (Hyd) • Puducherry • Vijayawada

Published by
Paras Medical Books Pvt. Ltd.

Registered Office:
5-1-473, Jambagh Road, Putlibowli, Hyderabad - 500095, Telangana, India.
Ph.: 040-2460-0869, 9348052516
E-mail: hyderabad@parasmedicalbooks.com

parasredkart.com
Your online medical books store

For Quick Single/Bulk Orders Send WhatsApp to (+91) 9912817189

Branch Offices:

Ameerpet (Hyderabad)	040-6678-5613;	+91 939-393-4080	*ameerpet@parasmedicalbooks.com*
Bangalore	080-2670-8108;	+91 934-281-2198	*bangalore@parasmedicalbooks.com*
Delhi	011-2325-2228;	+91 999-964-3040	*delhi@parasmedicalbooks.com*
Hyderguda (Hyderabad)	040-6681-7189;	+91 991-281-7189	*parasredkart@gmail.com*
Pondicherry	0413-224-1151;	+91 934-591-7522	*puducherry@parasmedicalbooks.com*
Vijayawada	0866-324-2002;	+91 939-379-8657	*vijaywada@parasmedicalbooks.com*

Associate Branch:

Pune	020-26054925; +91 9371781765	020-26124565;	*infoandorders@skotharimedicalbooks.com*

Obstetrics and Gynaecology – DNB Topic Wise Question Bank

by Mythri Sharan BK

Fourth Edition 2026
Third Edition 2023
Second Edition 2021
First Edition 2020

ISBN: 978-81-989441-7-7

Printed in Hyderabad, India

Dedication

To

My Mother

For her constant support and encouragement

Preface

Dear Students,

It gives me immense happiness to present the Fourth Edition of my book DNB Topic-Wise Question Bank in Obstetrics and Gynaecology. Each edition has been a step forward in simplifying and refining the way DNB aspirants prepare, and I am truly grateful for the continued love, trust, and feedback from students across India. Your appreciation and suggestions have been the inspiration behind every improvement made in this new edition.

In this edition, I have completely reorganized and simplified the content to make it more structured, precise, and student-friendly. Every major topic has been further divided into clear subtopics, making it easier for you to navigate, focus, and revise. The aim has been to help students understand at a glance what has been asked, how frequently it has appeared, and which areas require more attention.

Key Highlights of the Fourth Edition

- Complete restructuring: Each topic is divided into smaller, clearly defined subtopics for easy reference and better understanding.
- Updated questions: Includes all DNB university questions from June 2011 to June 2025.
- Smart marking system: ★ – Indicates questions asked repeatedly in the last 2–3 years.
- Recently added topics: A brand-new section has been introduced at the end, divided into Obstetrics, Foetal Medicine, Gynaecology, and Infertility, covering: Recently introduced and evolving areas in clinical practice, Latest technologies and innovations, Topics that have high chances of being asked in upcoming exams, even if not yet asked.
- Simplified layout: Cleaner presentation for quick reading and effective multiple revisions.

I strongly believe that success in postgraduate exams depends not only on hard work but also on smart preparation and repeated revision. Use this book to identify trends, track repeated questions, and strengthen your conceptual base.

I sincerely thank every student who has supported and guided me through each edition. Your continued encouragement keeps this book evolving to match the ever-changing patterns of examinations. I welcome your valuable feedback, corrections, or suggestions at: dr.mythrisharan@gmail.com

I hope this edition serves as your trusted companion and helps you approach your exams with clarity, confidence, and calmness.

With warm regards and best wishes

Mythri Sharan BK

Acknowledgements

I express my heartfelt gratitude to all my teachers and mentors from SRM Medical College, Chennai, Kasturba Medical College, Manipal, and St. Martha's Hospital, Bangalore, whose guidance has shaped my medical foundation and inspired me to pursue academic excellence.

I am deeply thankful to all the patients who have been my best teachers throughout my journey — their trust has been my greatest learning experience.

I owe everything I am today to my mother, Mrs. Anuradha, for her unconditional love, prayers, and constant encouragement at every step of my life, and to my sister Mrs. Mythili, for her endless support and belief in me.

My heartfelt thanks to my husband, Jai, for being my pillar of strength.

And to my little sunshine, Naira, who fills my world with love and joy — you inspire me every single day and remind me of life's true purpose.

My sincere thanks to Mr. Hitesh Kodnani of Paras Medical Books Pvt. Ltd. for his support and cooperation in publishing this edition.

As always, I thank God, for without His blessings, no effort can ever be truly successful.

Mythri Sharan B K

How To Use This Book

The Study Flow (follow this loop for every topic)

Textbook → Question Bank → Fill Gaps → Star & Prioritize → Revise → Next Topic

1. Complete the topic from your textbook.
2. Open the same topic in this Question Bank. Scan all questions at a glance.
3. Fill the gaps. If you see a question not fully covered in your textbook/class notes, go back and read that subtopic.
4. Focus on ★ questions. These are high-yield/repeated—give them priority.
5. Revise 2–3 times. Revision creates retention—and retention creates rank.
6. Repeat the loop for the next topic.

Worked Example: Fibroid (Uterine Leiomyoma)

Step 1: Complete textbook reading

- Core areas: definition, types/locations, symptoms, complications, evaluation, management (medical, interventional, surgical), fibroid in pregnancy, fertility/infertility, postoperative care, recent advances.

Step 2: Open "Fibroid" in this Question Bank

- Check all questions listed under Fibroid in one go.

Step 3: Fill the gaps (very important!)

- Example: You spot "Broad ligament fibroid" in the question list but your textbook section is brief/missing.

  → Go back to the textbook/standard reference and cover this subtopic now (clinical features, differentials, imaging, surgical approach, complications).
- Do this for every subtopic that appears as a question but isn't well covered in your notes.

Step 4: Star & prioritize

- Mark ★ questions (frequently asked/high-yield)

Step 5: Revise 2–3 times

- Rev-1: same day or within 24–48 hrs (fast scan of the question list).
- Rev-2: within 7–10 days (focus on ★ and weak subtopics).
- Rev-3: pre-exam polish (only ★ and your marked gaps).

Contents

(* signifies recently asked questions from 2023, 2024 & 2025)

Recent Advances

RECENT ADVANCES IN OBSTETRICS

- Stem cell therapy
- Non-invasive prenatal testing (NIPT / cfDNA-based screening)
- Uterine artery embolization in postpartum hemorrhage (PPH)
- Balloon occlusion, uterine compression sutures, and interventional radiology in PAS (Placenta Accreta Spectrum)
- Triple P procedure
- Cord blood and stem cell banking
- Non-invasive prenatal testing (NIPT / cfDNA-based screening)
- Newer biomarkers for preeclampsia (sFlt-1 / PlGF ratio)
- Advances in induction of labor and cervical ripening agents
- Precision obstetrics – individualized prediction for GDM, preeclampsia, PTL
- Management of obstetric hemorrhage – cell salvage, tranexamic acid updates
- Newer corticosteroid regimens and tocolytics for preterm birth
- Role of microbiome and probiotics in pregnancy outcomes
- Uterine transplantation and successful pregnancies
- Enhanced recovery after cesarean delivery (ERAC)
- Vaccination in pregnancy
- RPOC & AV malformations
- Role of Asprin in obstetrics
- Artificial intelligence and machine learning in OB-GYN (diagnostics, radiology, decision support)
- Electronic health record integration for obstetric risk prediction
- Flamm Geiger VBAC scoring system

RECENT ADVANCES IN FETAL MEDICINE

- Fetal DNA and non-invasive genetic testing (expanded NIPS panels, whole-genome cfDNA sequencing)

- Fetal MRI – Neurological evaluation
- 3D/4D/5D ultrasound and neurosonography
- Fetal echocardiography
- Fetal stem cell and gene therapy for hemoglobinopathies
- In-utero surgical correction of spina bifida and diaphragmatic hernia
- Fetoscopic laser ablation in twin-to-twin transfusion syndrome
- Radio-frequency ablation and cord occlusion procedures
- AI-assisted Doppler waveform analysis for placental insufficiency
- fetal anemia- Intrauterine blood transfusion
- Advances in diagnosis and management of non-immune hydrops

RECENT ADVANCES IN GYNECOLOGY

- Robotic surgeries
- Single-port laparoscopy
- Newer energy sources (Liga sure, robotic articulating instruments)
- Recurrent endometriosis – hormonal, immunomodulatory, and stem-cell approaches
- Gene therapy and molecular insights into endometriosis and fibroids
- Newer selective progesterone receptor modulators (SPRMs)
- Long-acting reversible contraception (LARC) – hormonal IUDs, injectables, vaginal rings
- New-generation oral contraceptives and transdermal systems
- Advances in hysteroscopy – tissue removal systems, morcellation
- Office-based hysteroscopy and outpatient procedures
- Uterine artery embolization and MR-guided focused ultrasound for fibroids
- Aesthetic/cosmetic gynaecology
- Ovarian rejuvenation using platelet-rich plasma (PRP)
- Vaginal laser and radiofrequency therapy for atrophy/laxity
- Immunotherapy and targeted therapy in ovarian and endometrial cancer (PARP inhibitors, pembrolizumab, etc.)
- cervical screening, digital colposcopy
- HPV nonavalent vaccine and updates in vaccination strategies
- Liquid-based cytology
- Enhanced recovery after gynecologic surgery (ERAS)
- Pelvic reconstructive and urogynecologic advances (robotic sacrocolpopexy, slings)

- Vaginal microbiome and probiotics for recurrent vaginitis
- POCSO ACT (Protection of children from sexual offences)
- Types of mesh and its role in pelvic organ prolapse
- Power morcellation in uterine fibroid
- Trans-genderism
- POF-premature ovarian failure

RECENT ADVANCES IN INFERTILITY AND REPRODUCTIVE MEDICINE

- Time lapse imaging of embryo in the IVF lab
- Genetic testing of embryos (PGT) – latest protocols
- Endometrial receptivity assay (ERA) and molecular profiling
- ART-Recent advances under ART ACT 2021
- Artificial intelligence in IVF prediction models
- Cryopreservation techniques – vitrification, oocyte/ovarian tissue banking
- Fertility preservation in oncology patients
- Uterine and ovarian transplantation – ethical & clinical outcomes
- Surrogacy updates
- Regenerative medicine in ovarian failure – stem cell and PRP therapy
- Andrology updates – DNA fragmentation testing and AI semen analysis
- Advances in luteal phase support and individualised stimulation protocols
- AMH and its role
- Pharmacogenomics in infertility drugs
- Minimal stimulation IVF and natural cycle IVF
- Recurrent implantation failure
- Fertility sparing treatment in young women with endometrial CA

CHAPTER

1

MENOPAUSE

MENOPAUSAL SYMPTOMS

1. A 49-year-old postmenopausal with hot flushes.
   a) Causes of vasomotor symptoms. *4+4(June 2025)*
   b) Counselling & management.

2. What are the clinical manifestations and diagnosis of menopause? *5 (Dec 2020)*

3. a) Define menopause. *2+4+4 (June 2020)*
   b) Urethral syndrome.
   c) Atrophic vaginitis.

4. a) Define menopause. *2+3+5 (June 2019)*
   b) Describe menopausal symptoms.
   c) Non-hormonal treatment for menopausal symptoms.

5. a) Define menopause. What is peri-menopausal transition? *3+4+3 (Dec 2011)*
   b) What is menopausal syndrome? Describe the management of hot flushes in menopause.
   c) Describe the role of local oestrogen therapy in a menopausal woman.

HRT

6. 49-year-old postmenopausal with hot flushes.
   Absolute contraindications to HRT. *2 (June 2025)*

7. a) Enlist various postmenopausal symptoms. *5+5 (May 2024)*
   b) Discuss the current status of hormone replacement therapy in menopause and various routes and dosages of hormone therapy.

8. a) What is 'genitourinary syndrome of menopause'? What are its symptoms? How does it affect the quality of life of a postmenopausal woman? *6+4 (June 2022)*
   b) Discuss the current status of hormonal & nonhormonal treatments for it.

9. a) Describe the endocrinology of climacteric and menopause.
   b) What is the role of hormone therapy for treatment of postmenopausal genitourinary symptoms?

c) What health screening and advice would you recommend for postmenopausal women? *5+2+3 (Dec 2018)*

10. Menopausal transition and health risk: current concepts on hormonal therapy in postmenopausal women. *5 (June 2017)*

11. a) Contemporary use of menopausal hormone therapy. *4+3+3 (April 2016)*
    b) Role of menopausal hormone therapy in gynaecological malignancies.
    c) Role of menopausal hormone therapy after hysterectomy with BSO for endometriosis.

12. a) Atrophic vaginitis. *5+5 (June 2015)*
    b) Current indications of HRT and the controversies.

13. a) Define menopause. *2+4+4 (Dec 2013)*
    b) What are the menopausal symptoms?
    c) What is the place of HRT in current scenario?

OSTEOPOROSIS

14. a) What is osteoporosis? *2+2+6 (June 2019)*
    b) Write about the prevention of post-menopausal osteoporosis.
    c) Diagnosis and management of post-menopausal osteoporosis.

15. a) What are the symptoms of menopause? *3+4+3 (Dec 2016)*
    b) Treatment of vasomotor symptoms of menopause.
    c) Prevention of post-menopausal osteoporosis.

16. a) Pathophysiology of osteoporosis in post-menopausal women.
    b) Prevention, diagnosis & management of post-menopausal osteoporosis. *3+ (2+2+3) (June 2016)*

17. a) Role of gynaecologist in prevention of osteoporosis in postmenopausal women. *7+3 (June 2014)*
    b) What drugs can be used for its treatment?

18. a) What are the factors affecting bone health in postmenopausal women?
    b) Discuss preventive strategies for postmenopausal osteoporosis.
    c) How do you diagnose postmenopausal osteoporosis? *3+4+3 (June 2013)*

POSTMENOPAUSAL BLEEDING

19. a) What are the causes of postmenopausal bleeding? *2+8 (June 2021)*
    b) How will you manage a case of 60 year lady with dirty foul smelling discharge with postcoital bleeding?

CHAPTER

2

INFERTILITY

MALE INFERTILITY

Sperm Analysis

1. a) What is the difference between Spermatogenesis & Spermiogenesis?
   b) What changes occur in the sperm before fertilization?
   c) Compare the WHO 2010 and WHO 2021 criteria for semen analysis.
   2+2+6 (Oct 2024)

2. WHO criteria for normal semen analysis. *5 (Dec 2018)*

3. a) Enumerate the minimal criteria, as laid down by the WHO on a normal semen analysis. *4+3 (Dec 2011)*
   b) Draw the structure of a mature spermatozoon.

CAUSES OF MALE INFERTILITY

4. a) Causes of male factor infertility. *3+4 (June 2025)*
   b) Workup of male infertility.

5. a) Enumerate causes of male factor infertility. *3+7 (Dec 2022)*
   b) Describe evaluation and management of tubal infertility.

6. a) What are the causes of male infertility? *3+3+4 (June 2013)*
   b) Describe the normal semen parameters.
   c) How will you manage an infertile couple with oligospermia in male partner?

SPERM ABNORMALITIES

7. Management of azoospermia. *3 (June 2025)*

8. Interpretation and management of abnormal semen report. *5 (June 2020)*

9. a) Define azoospermia. *2+2 (June 2019)*
   b) Types of azoospermia.

10. Evaluation of patient with azoospermia. *5 (Dec 2018)*

11. Evaluation of male partner with oligospermia. *6 (Dec 2017)*

12. Enumerate causes of azoospermia. *3 (Dec 2011)*

SPERM RETRIEVAL TECHNIQUES

13. Sperm retrieval techniques. *6 (June 2019)*

14. Sperm retrieval techniques. *5 (Dec 2016)*

15. Sperm retrieval techniques in assisted reproduction. *5 (June 2015)*

OTHERS

16.a) How will you evaluate semen sample? *5+5 (June 2014)*
   b) What are the treatment options available for male factor infertility?

17.a) What are the indications of IUI? *4+6 (Dec 2014)*
   b) Write briefly about different methods of semen preparation.

18. Intrauterine insemination (IUI). *4 (Dec 2017)*

PRIMARY INFERTILITY

19.a) Define primary infertility and its causes.
   b) Describe the investigations to be done in a couple, married for 5 years, with infertility. *5+5 (April 2023)*

SECONDARY INFERTILITY

20.a) Describe the aetiologies of secondary infertility.
   b) Discuss the management of a couple both 32 years old with 4 years of infertility. The female partner has history of weight gain, delayed menses with scanty flow. *4+6 (May 2024)*

21.a) Describe the aetiologies of secondary infertility. *4+6 (June 2022)*
   b) Discuss the management of a couple both 32 years old with 6 years of secondary infertility following 2 abortions and no living issue with a married life of 8 years.

22. A 30 year old lady presents with history of two miscarriages and inability to conceive *(3+3)+4 (Dec 2013)*
   a) Discuss the possible causes and their evaluation.
   b) How would you manage tubal block?

UNEXPLAINED INFERTILITY

23.a) Define unexplained infertility. *2+4+4 (June 2018)*

b) Discuss the role of laparo-hysteroscopy in women with unexplained infertility.
c) How will you manage a woman with unexplained infertility?

24. Unexplained infertility. *5 (Dec 2016)*

OVULATION INDUCTION

25.a) Causes of anovulation. *4+4+2 (June 2025)*
b) Doppler role in infertility.
c) Complications of ovulation induction.

26.a) What is the induction of ovulation? *3+3+4 (June 2020)*
b) Enumerate the protocols of induction of ovulation?
c) Prevention and management of hyperstimulation syndrome.

27.a) How will you induce ovulation in PCOS. *5+5 (Dec 2019)*
b) Prevention & management of ovarian hyperstimulation syndrome (OHSS).

28.a) Controlled ovarian stimulation and monitoring of follicular growth.
b) Prevention of OHSS. *5+5 (Dec 2015)*

OVARIAN HYPERSTIMULATION SYNDROME (OHSS)

29.a) Define and classify Ovarian Hyperstimulation Syndrome (OHSS).
b) Discuss management of severe OHSS and newer agents in management of OHSS. *3+7 (Oct 2023)*

30.a) What is OHSS? Discuss its prevention & management. *5+5 (April 2023)*
b) Describe the role of Assisted Reproductive Technology in unexplained infertility women.

31.a) What are the different tests for diagnosis of ovulation?
b) Diagnosis and management of OHSS.
c) Prevention of OHSS. *3+5+2 (Dec 2020)*

32.a) What is induction of ovulation? *3+3+4 (June 2020)*
b) Enumerate the protocols of induction of ovulation.
c) Prevention and management of hyperstimulation syndrome.

33. Ovarian hyperstimulation syndrome. *5 (June 2020)*

34.a) Define OHSS. *2+4+4 (April 2016)*
b) What are the risk factors?
c) How you manage the case of OHSS?

35.a) Controlled ovarian stimulation and monitoring of follicular growth.
b) Prevention of OHSS. *5+5 (Dec 2015)*

36. A 32 year woman with PCOS has successful IVF conception. Within a few days of embryo transfer, she presents in the emergency with nausea, vomiting, breathlessness and abdominal pain. *2+5+3 (Dec 2018)*
a) What is your diagnosis?
b) Give an outline of your management plan.
c) How can this complication be prevented?

TUBAL FACTORS

37.a) Utero-tubal peritoneal factors for infertile women. *2+8 (June 2019)*
b) Role of hysteroscopic surgery in infertility.

38.a) Assessment of tubal factors in infertility. *3+3+4 (Dec 2016)*
b) Role of clipping in hydrosalpinx before IVF.
c) Tubal recanalization in modern era.

39.a) What are microbial aetiologies of acute salpingitis? *3+4+3 (April 2016)*
b) Diagnosis and laparoscopic grading of acute salpingitis.
c) Justify that delayed care is a risk factor for impaired infertility.

40.a) Role of surgery for the tubal factors of infertility? *5+5 (Dec 2015)*
b) Management of unexplained infertility.

41. A 30 year old lady with history of 2 miscarriages and inability to conceive.
a) Discuss the possible causes and their evaluation. *3+3+4 (Dec 2013)*
b) How would you manage tubal block?

GENITAL TUBERCULOSIS

42.a) Cause of infertility in genital tuberculosis. *5+5 (June 2021)*
b) Diagnosis of genital tuberculosis.

43.a) Genital tuberculosis and infertility? *5 (Dec 2016)*

ENDOMETRIOSIS & INFERTILITY

44.a) What is the role of minimally invasive surgery in case of endometriosis?
b) Discuss the management of recurrent endometriosis in infertility.
5+5 (June 2018)

45. Management of endometrioma in a young infertile woman. *5 (Dec 2016)*

46.a) What is the pathophysiology of infertility in cases of endometriosis?
b) Critically evaluate the advantages and disadvantages of various modes of therapy in young women having endometriosis. *4+6 (June 2016)*

47.a) How does mild endometriosis contribute to subfertility? *5+5 (June 2014)*
b) How can you improve the chances of pregnancy in these cases?

ASSISTED REPRODUCTIVE TECHNIQUES (ARTs)

48.a) Types of ART. *4+4+2 (June 2025)*
b) Surrogacy Amendments Rule 2024 – key points.
c) Punishment for violation.

49.a) What are the strategies to limit the multiple gestation risk of assisted reproductive technology? *5+5 (Dec 2020)*
b) Foetal reduction

50. Indications and challenges of elective single embryo transfer (eSET). *5 (June 2020)*

51.a) Describe the different markers of ovarian reserve. *5+5 (Dec 2019)*
b) What are the indications of IVF-ICSI?

52.a) What is preimplantation genetic testing (PGT)? *5+5 (Dec 2019)*
b) Applications in ART.

53.a) What is ART? *2+4+4 (June 2018)*
b) What are the different components of IVF cycle?
c) How can you prevent ovarian hyper stimulation syndrome?

54.a) Time lapse imaging of embryo in the IVF lab? *5+5 (Dec 2016)*
b) Complications of ART.

55.a) What is ART? *1+3+3+3 (Dec 2013)*
b) Which techniques are included in ART?
c) What are the recent guidelines for ART?
d) Give your comments on pre-implantation genetic diagnosis.

CRYOPRESERVATION

56. Discuss cryopreservation of embryo and oocyte, length of successful preservation and what influences rates of successful pregnancy outcome. *10 (Dec 2022)*

57. Ovarian tissue cryopreservation. *5 (Dec 2020)*

58.a) Role of cryo-freezing in ART. *5+5 (Dec 2015)*
b) What are the risk factors?

59. Role of cryo-freezing in assisted reproductive technologies. *5 (June 2015)*

SURROGACY

60.a) Describe the components and recent changes under Assisted Reproductive Technology (Regulation) Act, 2021. *5+5 (May 2024)*
b) Discuss the pros and cons of Surrogacy (Regulation) Act, 2021.

61. ICMR Guidelines for Surrogacy in India. *5 (April 2023)*

62.a) Describe the components of 'The Surrogacy (Regulation) Act, 2021'.
b) What were the challenges of commercial surrogacy?
c) What are the negative points of the Act? *6+2+2 (June 2022)*

63.a) What is Surrogacy and what are its medical indications?
b) Ethical issues in the Surrogacy Bill. *5+5 (Dec 2020)*

64.a) What is surrogacy and what are the medical indications?
b) Ethical issues in surrogacy bill *5+5 (Dec 2019)*

65.a) Assessment of embryo quality in ART. *5+5 (Dec 2015)*
b) Situations to suggest surrogacy.

66.a) What is surrogacy? *3+3+4 (Dec 2014)*
b) How will you take consent and prepare surrogate for IVF-ET?

PHYSIOLOGY IN INFERTILITY

66.a) Describe the physiology of menstruation.
b) Discuss the management of anovulatory infertility. *4+6 (April 2023)*

67.a) Indicators of ovarian reserve. *4 (June 2020)*

68.a) Describe hypothalamo-pituitary ovarian axis. *5 (June 2020)*
b) How will you treat hypogonadotropic hypoestrogenic infertility?

69.a) What is LH surge? *2+2+2+4 (June 2019)*
b) Functions of LH surge.
c) Indications of surrogate LH surge.
d) Methods of ovulation trigger.

70.a) Endometrium in menstrual cycle. *3+3+4 (June 2019)*

b) What is Uterine Biophysical profile (UBP)?

c) Role of ultrasound and colour Doppler for assessment of UBP.

71.a) What is ovarian reserve? *2+3+5 (Dec 2015)*

b) Its role in infertility.

c) Outline the management of an infertile woman who is a poor responder.

72.a) What is ovarian reserve? *3+3+4 (June 2014)*

b) How can we test for ovarian reserve?

c) What is the significance of Anti Mullerian hormone (AMH)?

CHAPTER

3

REPRODUCTIVE ENDOCRINOLOGY

PRIMARY AMENORRHOEA

1. Workup of 17-year-old girl with secondary sexual characters & primary amenorrhea. *4 (June 2025)*

2. a) Tanner staging. *2+4+4(June 2025)*
   b) Tanner staging of breast.
   c) Turner's syndrome.

3. How will you manage an 18-year-old girl presenting with primary amenorrhea? *6 (Oct 2024)*

4. a) Enumerate causes of primary amenorrhea. *4+6 (Dec 2022)*
   b) How will you manage androgen insensitivity syndrome at 17 years age?

5. a) Define primary amenorrhea. *2+4+4 (June 2022)*
   b) Enlist various aetiologies of primary amenorrhea.
   c) Describe the workup of a case of primary amenorrhea in methodical manner.

6. a) Define primary Amenorrhoea. *2+2+6 (June 2019)*
   b) Enumerate causes for primary amenorrhoea.
   c) Turner's syndrome.

7. a) Essential requirements for onset & continuation of normal menstruation.
   b) Causes of crypto-menorrhoea?
   c) Evaluation of a 17 year old girl presenting with primary amenorrhoea. *3+3+4 (Dec 2015)*

8. a) Define primary amenorrhoea. *2+2+ (3+3) (June 2014)*
   b) Enumerate its causes.
   c) How will you work up and manage such a case?

SECONDARY AMENORRHOEA

9. a) Define secondary amenorrhea. *2+4+4 (May 2024)*
   b) Enlist various causes of secondary amenorrhea.

c) Describe the workup of a case of secondary amenorrhea as a flow chart.

10.a) Define secondary amenorrhoea. *2+3+5 (June 2016)*

b) Enlist its causes.

c) Plan of management of a case of secondary amenorrhoea using a flow chart.

11.a) Define secondary amenorrhoea. *2+3+5 (Dec 2014)*

b) Enumerate its causes.

c) How will you work up a case of secondary amenorrhoea?

12.a) Define secondary amenorrhoea. *1+3+6 (Dec 2013)*

b) Enlist its causes.

c) How will you evaluate a 28 year old lady with history of secondary amenorrhoea since last delivery 5 years ago?

13.a) Define secondary amenorrhoea. Enlist its causes. *1+2+3+4 (Dec 2012)*

b) What is galactorrhoea amenorrhoea syndrome?

c) Outline the principles of management of galactorrhoea amenorrhoea in a 24 year old woman.

PUBERTY

14.a) Describe the physiological changes during puberty. *5+5 (April 2023)*

b) How will you evaluate a 17-year-old girl who has yet not attained puberty?

15.a) What is precocious puberty? *3+3+4 (June 2021)*

b) Enumerate the causes of precocious puberty.

c) Outline the management of precocious puberty in 7-year-old girl.

16.a) Physiology of puberty. *3+2+5 (Dec 2020)*

b) Causes of delayed puberty.

c) Management of delayed puberty.

17.a) Hormonal and physical changes during puberty. *4+3+3 (June 2018)*

b) What are the different causes of precocious puberty?

c) Make an outline for the management of case with precocious puberty.

18.a) Define precocious puberty. *1+4+5 (Dec 2016)*

b) What are the causes of precocious puberty?

c) Outline its management.

19.a) What are the causes of delayed puberty. *5+5 (Dec 2016)*
b) Give an algo rhythmic clinical approach to an adolescent girl with delayed puberty.

20.a) Differential diagnosis of delayed pubertal development.
b) How will you investigate delayed pubertal development in 16 years old girl? *5+5 (June 2015)*

21.a) Define puberty. *1+3+ (3+3) (Dec 2013)*
b) What are the causes of precocious puberty?
c) Discuss the evaluation and management of a 7 year old girl with precocious puberty.

22. Describe the sequence of various changes during puberty. *2 (June 2012)*

23.a) Enumerate the causes of puberty menorrhagia. *2+3+5 (June 2012)*
b) Describe the management of puberty menorrhagia.
c) Differential diagnosis of puberty menorrhagia.

OVULATORY DISORDERS

24.a) Classify ovulatory disorders.
b) Describe the management of anovulatory cycles in a 30 year old woman. *4+6 (Dec 2022)*

PCOS

25.a) What is the etiopathogenesis of PCOS? *3+3+4 (April 2023)*
b) Enumerate the long-term complication of PCOS.
c) Discuss the management of young lady with hirsutism.

26.a) Discuss the diagnostic criteria for PCOS. *2+8 (June 2021)*
b) Describe the management of adolescent lady with PCOS.

27. Outline the diagnostic evaluation of polycystic ovary syndrome in adolescents. *10 (Dec 2020)*

28.a) How will you induce ovulation in PCOS?
b) Prevention and management of ovarian hyperstimulation syndrome (OHSS) *5+5 (Dec 2019)*

29. Biochemical and endocrinological profile in young women with PCOS and its impact on infertility. *5 (June 2017)*

30. A young girl of 17 year of age has obesity and oligomenorrhoea. What is your provisional diagnosis? What are the investigations to be done and advice regarding the management? *3+2+ (2+3) (June 2015)*

HIRSUTISM

31.a) Define hirsutism. How do you grade it? *3+3+4 (June 2022)*

b) Workup of a 20 year old woman presenting with hirsutism.

c) Write the summary of the guidelines recommended by Endocrine Society.

32. A 25 year unmarried woman presents in the gynaecology clinic with excessive hair growth on the face. *2+4+4 (Dec 2018)*

a) Enumerate the various causes of Hirsutism.

b) Discuss the workup in this patient.

c) What are the common drugs used for treatment of hirsutism? State at least 2 side effects of each of these drugs.

33. Write the causes, investigations and management of a young girl with hirsutism. *3+4+3 (June 2014)*

HYPERPROLACTINEMIA

34.a) Describe the clinical presentation of a case of hyperprolactinemia.

b) Discuss the work up and management of a case of hyperprolactinemia. *4+6 (May 2024)*

35.a) What are the causes of hyperprolactinemia? *5+5 (Dec 2019)*

b) Management of hyperprolactinemia.

PREMATURE OVARIAN INSUFFICIENCY (POI)

36.a) Describe the criteria for diagnosis of POI. *2+8 (Dec 2022)*

b) Discuss evaluation and management of POI.

37.a) Describe the various tests to measure ovarian reserve.

b) Enlist the various causes of premature ovarian failure.

c) Discuss the long term clinical implications in a case of premature ovarian failure. *3+3+4 (June 2022)*

38. Causes of primary ovarian insufficiency. *5 (Dec 2020)*

39.a) Define premature ovarian failure (POF). *2+4+4 (June 2017)*

b) Its etiological factors, consequences and impact on health.

c) How will you diagnose and manage POF?

40.a) Various methods to assess ovarian reserve. *4+2+4 (April 2016)*

b) Enumerate the causes of chromosomally competent ovarian failure.

c) How will you manage a 22-year-old woman with premature ovarian failure?

41.a) Causes of premature ovarian failure (POF). *3+3+4 (June 2015)*
b) How will you evaluate a case of POF?
c) Therapeutic options and management of a case of POF with infertility.

MULLERIAN ANOMALIES

42.a) ESHRE/ESGE consensus on classification of female genital tract anomalies. *5+5 (June 2025)*
b) Differentiate arcuate, septate, bicorporeal uterus on 3D USG (with diagrams).

43.a) Enumerate the classification of mullerian anomalies. *3+3 (Oct 2023)*
b) Discuss the obstetric significance of various mullerian anomalies.

44.a) Classify Mullerian duct anomalies. *4+3+3 (Dec 2021)*
b) What are the clinical problems associated with Mullerian duct anomalies?
c) Outline the management of haematocolpos with transverse vaginal septum in an adolescent girl.

45.a) Describe the embryological development of the female reproductive tract in brief. *5+5 (June 2020)*
b) Discuss diagnosis and management of bicornuate uterus.

46.a) Development of Mullerian duct. *5+5 (Dec 2019)*
b) Importance of anti-Mullerian hormone

47.a) New classification of congenital uterine anomalies. *4+6 (Dec 2019)*
b) Management of hysteroscopic septal resection and its complications.

48.a) Development of Mullerian duct. *3+3+4 (June 2018)*
b) Classify different types of Mullerian anomalies.
c) How will you diagnose various Mullerian anomalies?

49.a) Classify Mullerian duct anomalies. What are the associated renal tract anomalies? *5+5 (June 2017)*
b) How will you investigate and manage a case of crypto menorrhoea?

50.a) Outline the current classification of Mullerian agenesis.
b) Role of vaginoplasty in Mullerian agenesis.
c) How would you manage a patient with complete androgen insensitivity syndrome? *3+3+4 (April 2016)*

51.a) Classify Mullerian abnormalities. *3+ (4+3) (June 2015)*
b) Problems of reproduction in women with Mullerian abnormalities and their management.

52.a) Classify Mullerian abnormalities. *3+ (4+3) (Dec 2014)*

b) How will you investigate and manage a young pubertal girl suspected of such a problem?

53.a) Classify Mullerian anomalies and enumerate their significance in Obstetrics & Gynaecology. *(3+2)+ (2+3) (June 2014)*

b) How will you diagnose and manage a case of intrauterine septum?

54.a) Classify Mullerian duct anomalies. *2+4+4 (June 2013)*

b) What are its clinical features?

c) Outline the management of haematocolpos with transverse vaginal septum in an adolescent girl.

55.a) How will you classify the Mullerian duct anomalies? *2+3+2+3 (Dec 2012)*

b) Show the different anomalies diagrammatically.

c) Enumerate various gynaecological and obstetrical problems caused by these anomalies.

d) Outline the plan of management of a septate uterus.

TRANSGENDERISM

56.a) What is gender dysphoria in teenagers? *2+8 (June 2021)*

b) Discuss the issues and management of transgender adolescents.

CHAPTER

4

BENIGN GYNAECOLOGY

VAGINAL INFECTIONS

1. a) Discuss the causes and management of pruritus vulvae.
   b) Detection and management of bacterial vaginosis. *6+4 (April 2023)*

2. Management of recurrent vulvovaginal candidiasis. *5 (June 2020)*

3. a) What are normal defence mechanisms of genital tract?
   b) What are the causes of pruritus vulva?
   c) Diagnosis and management of moniliasis. *2+2+6 (June 2019)*

4. a) Distinguish between physiological and pathological vaginal discharge.
   b) How will you evaluate vaginal discharge to accurately make a diagnosis in a woman of reproductive age group?
   c) Therapy for various vaginal discharges. *(2+2) +3+3 (Dec 2016)*

5. a) Describe normal vaginal ecosystem. *3+2+5 (June 2014)*
   b) What are the consequences of its abnormalities?
   c) How will you diagnose and manage a case of bacterial vaginosis?

6. a) What is the constitution of vaginal discharge in a young woman?
   b) Describe the protective mechanism against ascending infection in female genital tract.
   c) Outline the management of vulvo-vaginal candidiasis. *3+3+4 (June 2013)*

7. Enumerate the normal flora of vagina. *3 (June 2012)*

8. a) What are the predisposing factors for vulvo-vaginal candidiasis?
   b) How do you diagnose it?
   c) Work up plan for a woman having recurrent candidiasis.
   d) Treatment of recurrent vulvo-vaginal candidiasis. *4+2+4 (June 2012)*

PID

9. a) Mrs Q presents with features of acute PID. Discuss the complications and sequelae of this condition. *3+4+3 (Dec 2021)*

b) Discuss the CDC guidelines for diagnosis of acute PID and indications for hospitalisation.

c) Discuss contraception and risk of pelvic inflammatory disease (PID).

10.a) Enumerate the etiological factors of pelvic inflammatory disease in a young woman of reproductive age. *2+4+4 (June 2017)*

b) What are its symptoms, signs and management?

c) Its long term consequences and their prevention.

11.a) Write the CDC criteria for diagnosing PID. *3+2+5 (June 2016)*

b) What are the indication of hospitalization in PID?

c) How will you manage the hospitalized PID patient?

12.a) What are microbial aetiologies of acute salpingitis? *3+4+3 (April 2016)*

b) Diagnosis and laparoscopic grading of acute salpingitis.

c) Justify that delayed care is a risk factor for impaired infertility.

13.a) What do you understand by PID (pelvic inflammatory disease)?

b) How will you investigate and manage it? *4+ (3+3) (Dec 2014)*

14.a) What are the etiological factors of acute PID? *3+4+3 (June 2013)*

b) What are its clinical features and differential diagnosis?

c) Describe its treatment and sequel.

PELVIC PAIN

15. A 26-year-old female present P1L1 with acute lower abdominal pain since 3 hours with history of irregular periods. She has a history of chronic pelvic pain for past 1 year following LSCS done 18 months back and has received treatment for Kochs.

Discuss differential diagnosis and management. *10 (Dec 2022)*

16.a) Define chronic pelvic pain.

b) Discuss the causes and management of chronic pelvic pain in women of reproductive age. *2+8 (Aug 2021)*

17.a) What are ovarian remnant and residual ovary syndrome?

b) Give causes of chronic pelvic pain.

c) Management of a 28-year-old lady with CPP, dyspareunia and congestive dysmenorrhoea. *2+2+6 (June 2019)*

18.a) Define chronic pelvic pain (CPP). *2+4+4 (Dec 2018)*

b) Discuss the causes of CPP.

c) Outline the management plan.

19.a) Define chronic pelvic pain. *4+2+4 (Dec 2016)*
b) What are the possible contributory factors for chronic pelvic pain?
c) How will you investigate and manage chronic pelvic pain in a 27 year old lady with secondary infertility?

20.a) Causes of acute pelvic pain in women. *4+6 (June 2015)*
b) How would you manage a 21 years old lady with acute pelvic pain?

AUB (ABNORMAL UTERINE BLEEDING)

21.a) Define heavy menstrual bleeding (FIGO). *2+4+4 (June 2025)*
b) PBAC chart.
c) Classify AUB.

FIBROIDS

22.a) FIGO classification of fibroid uterus. *5+5 (June 2025)*
b) Guidelines for removing submucous fibroid.

ADENOMYOSIS

23.a) Clinical features of adenomyosis. *3+4+3 (June 2025)*
b) USG findings.
c) Medical management.

OVARIAN CYST

24. 43-year-old with large abdominal lump.
a) Differential diagnoses. *2+4+4 (June 2025)*
b) Confirm diagnosis.
c) Compare malignancy indices.

25.a) Describe the PALM-COEIN terminology for abnormal uterine bleeding.
b) Discuss the workup of a case of abnormal uterine bleeding in a 45-year-old multiparous lady. *4+6 (May 2024)*

26. PALM COEIN Classification of abnormal uterine bleeding. *2 (June 2021)*

27.a) Describe the PALM COEIN classification of abnormal uterine bleeding.
b) Describe the non-surgical methods of managing uterine fibroids. *5+5 (Dec 2019)*

28.a) What are the causes of heavy menstrual bleeding (HMB)?
b) How will you evaluate a case of abnormal HMB in a 32-year multiparous woman?

c) What are the medical modalities available in management of a case of HMB? *4+3+3 (June 2018)*

29.a) What is FIGO classification of system (PALM-COEIN) for causes of abnormal uterine bleeding in non-gravid women of reproductive age?

b) Management of AUB-A in a case of heavy menstrual bleeding in 38 years old woman. *6+4 (Dec 2016)*

30.a) What is the physiology for controlling menstrual blood loss at endometrial level? *3+4+3 (June 2014)*

b) How will you evaluate a case of heavy menstrual bleeding?

c) What are the non-surgical management options available in a case of fibroid uterus?

31.a) Enumerate the causes of menometrorrhagia in a 45 year old multipara

b) How will you investigate her?

c) Outline the management of sub-mucous fibroid polyp. *3+4+3 (June 2013)*

ENDOMETRIAL HYPERPLASIA

32.a) Endometrial hyperplasia and its associations. *5+5 (Dec 2019)*

b) Management of a perimenopausal women with simple cystic hyperplasia.

33. A 30 year P1L1 has abnormal uterine bleeding. HPE of endometrial sample reveals hyperplasia with atypia. She desires to retain her fertility.

a) List the factors predisposing to endometrial hyperplasia.

b) Management options that you can offer to her.

c) Outline her follow up protocol. *2+5+3 (Dec 2018)*

33. a) What are the different types of endometrial hyperplasia?

b) Describe briefly the prognosis of each type.

c) How will you manage different types of endometrial hyperplasia in a peri-menopausal woman? *2+3+5 (June 2018)*

34.a) What is endometrial hyperplasia? *1+5+4 (June 2016)*

b) Classify endometrial hyperplasia, indicating their malignant potential.

c) Outline the principles of management of atypical hyperplasia.

FIBROIDS

35.a) FIGO classification of fibroid uterus. *5+5 (June 2025)*

b) Guidelines for removing submucous fibroid.

36.a) Describe FIGO Classification of fibromyoma. *3+4+3 (April 2023)*

b) What are the criteria and methods for hysteroscopic myomectomy?

c) Discuss various measures to reduce blood loss at myomectomy.

37. Mrs. W, nulligravida, presented with history of heavy menstrual bleeding and inability to conceive. Examination revealed a large myoma at the fundus of the uterus.

a) Justify the surgical management that you would opt in this case.

b) Discuss the preoperative preparation & complications of the procedure.

3+4+3 (Dec 2021)

38. How will you classify and manage a case of fibroid uterus? *8 (Aug 2021)*

39.a) What are the various non-surgical methods of treatment of leiomyoma?

b) Discuss the advantages and disadvantages of each method.

5+5 (June 2018)

40. A 45 year old woman had abdominal hysterectomy for cervical fibroid. She had anuria in postoperative period. *3+5+2 (June 2016)*

a) What are the possible causes of anuria?

b) Outline the principles of management.

c) What complications can occur in her?

41.a) What measures can be taken to minimize blood loss during myomectomy? *3+3+4 (April 2016)*

b) What is leiomyomatosis?

c) Role of power morcellation in uterine fibroid.

42.a) Discuss recent classification for abnormal uterine bleeding (AUB).

b) Briefly outline the management of fibromyoma. *6+4 (Dec 2014)*

43.a) Describe the types of cervical fibroid. *4+3+3 (Dec 2013)*

b) What are the complications anticipated during surgery for cervical fibroid and how will you prevent them?

44.a) Outline the strategies to minimize blood loss intra-operatively during myomectomy. *4+3+3 (June 2012)*

b) Enumerate factors which favour a myomectomy procedure in reproductive age group.

c) Discuss present status of uterine artery embolization in fibroid uterus.

DYSMENORRHOEA

45.a) Define dysmenorrhea, types and describe the aetiology of dysmenorrhea.

b) Discuss the management of vaginismus in different age groups.

5+5 (Dec 2022)

ENDOMETRIOSIS

46.a) Describe the various clinical presentations of endometriosis.
b) Discuss the management options for a woman with symptomatic endometriosis.
c) Detail the revised American Society for Reproductive Medicine (rASRM) classification for endometriosis. *3+4+3 (May 2024)*

47.a) Describe the etiopathogenesis of endometriosis. *5+5 (April 2023)*
b) How will you manage a case of recurrent endometriosis?

48.a) Describe classification of endometriosis. *4+3+3 (Dec 2022)*
b) Discuss non-invasive diagnosis of endometriosis.
c) Treatment of a 32 year old after definitive surgery for endometriosis.

49.a) Discuss the aetiology and clinical features of endometriosis.
b) What are the indications for surgery in case of endometriosis?
c) Discuss the surgical management of endometriosis. *4+2+4 (Dec 2021)*

50. Challenges and precautions during laparoscopic cystectomy of bilateral large endometriosis in an infertile woman. *6 (June 2020)*

51.a) Theories on pathogenesis of endometriosis. *3+7 (Dec 2019)*
b) Genetic basis of endometriosis.

52.a) Medical management of endometriosis. *4+3+3 (Dec 2018)*
b) What is the role of laparoscopy in endometriosis?
c) Describe the fertility work up in a lady with endometriosis.

53.a) Define endometriosis. *1+ (2+3) +4 (April 2016)*
b) Etio-pathogenesis and diagnostic modalities of endometriosis.
c) Nonsurgical management of endometriosis.

54. Discuss aetiology of endometriosis and role of laparoscopy in its diagnosis. *5+5 (Dec 2014)*

55.a) Define endometriosis. *2+4+4 (Dec 2013)*
b) Discuss the aetiology, clinical features and medical management of endometriosis.

OVARIAN CYST

56. Discuss the management of adnexal mass in pregnancy. *5 (April 2023)*

57.a) What are the causes of lower abdominal lump in a 13 year old adolescent girl? *2+4+4 (June 2017)*

b) Clinical and investigative approach in this girl to arrive at a diagnosis.
c) How will you manage ovarian dermoid cyst in this young girl?

ECTOPIC PREGNANCY

58.a) Medical management of ectopic pregnancy.
b) Caesarean scar pregnancy. *5+5 (Dec 2020)*

59. Recent advances in the management of tubal ectopic pregnancy. *10 (June 2020)*

60.a) List the various modalities of treatment of ectopic pregnancy.
b) What is the criteria for patient selection for medical management of ectopic pregnancy?
c) Discuss various surgical procedures performed in management of ectopic pregnancy. *2+2+6 (June 2018)*

61.a) What are the different types of ectopic pregnancy? *3+3+4 (Dec 2018)*
b) Assessment of the above patient in emergency.
c) Medical management of ectopic pregnancy.

62. Diagnosis and management of early unruptured tubal ectopic pregnancy. *5 (June 2017)*

63.a) Diagnosis of unruptured tubal ectopic pregnancy. *4+3+3 (Dec 2015)*
b) Expectant management for unruptured tubal ectopic pregnancy.
c) Persistent trophoblastic activity following management of ectopic pregnancy.

64.a) Define ectopic pregnancy and enumerate the types of ectopic pregnancy.
b) What are the reasons for increased prevalence of ectopic pregnancy?
c) How will you manage a case of unruptured ectopic pregnancy in nulliparous patient? *(1+2)+3+4 (Dec 2013)*

PELVIC TB

65.a) Describe the etiopathogenesis of genital tuberculosis. *5+5 (April 2023)*
b) How will you diagnose and treat a case of genital tuberculosis?

66.a) Discuss role of Laser in Gynaecology. *3+5 (Dec 2021)*
b) How will you investigate a case of suspected genital tuberculosis?

67.a) What are the clinical manifestations of pelvic tuberculosis?
b) How will you diagnose pelvic tuberculosis?
c) Treatment of pelvic tuberculosis. *3+4+3 (June 2018)*

68.a) Clinical features of genital tuberculosis in young women of reproductive age group. *3+4+3 (Dec 2015)*
b) Recent advances in laboratory diagnosis of genital tuberculosis.
c) Indications for surgery in women having genital tuberculosis.

69.a) Critically evaluate the various Nuclear Amplification Assays (NAA) in the diagnosis of endometrial tuberculosis. *3+3+4 (June 2012)*
b) Define MDR-tuberculosis and XDR-tuberculosis. What are the difficulties in the management of such cases?
c) What are the treatment options and their success rates for a case of genital tuberculosis with infertility?

STD & GENITAL ULCERS

70.a) Normal vaginal microbial flora. *5+5 (Dec 2019)*
b) Treatment of recurrent vulvovaginal candidiasis.

71.a) Enumerate the causes of vulval ulcers. *2+3+2+3 (June 2017)*
b) How will you clinically evaluate a case and how will you proceed to confirm your diagnosis?
c) Outline its management.

72.a) What are the different types of genital ulcers. *3+4 (April 2016)*
b) Clinical presentation in relation to specific diagnosis of genital ulcer.

73.a) What are the types of sexually transmitted genital ulcers?
b) Describe their clinical presentations.
c) How will you confirm the diagnosis? *3+4+3 (June 2014)*

PYOMETRA

74. Pyometra: Diagnosis and management. *5 (June 2015)*

75.a) Define pyometra. *2+3+5 (June 2012)*
b) Enlist its causes.
c) Outline the management plan for pyometra.

OTHERS

76. A 34-year-old female patient with moderate anaemia presented with complaints of something coming out per vaginum since 8 months post a normal vaginal delivery conducted by a Dai. She has also irregular bleeding since then.

Discuss differential diagnosis and management. *10 (Dec 2022)*

77.a) What is vulvodynia? *2+2+6 (June 2019)*

b) Classification of vulvodynia.

c) Management of localized vulvodynia.

78.a) List the causes of pruritus vulvae. *3+4+3 (Dec 2018)*

b) How will you manage a woman presenting with white patch on labia minora?

c) What is the role of colposcopy in management of vulval lesions?

79. Prophylactic salpingectomy. *5 (June 2016)*

80.a) Enumerate the causes of post-coital bleeding. *2+4+4 (June 2016)*

b) How will you investigate and manage a 45 year old woman having post coital bleeding?

81.a) Parameters a gynaecologist should utilize during assessment of a 60 year old woman who comes for a health check-up. Give reasons for your choice. *3+3+4 (June 2015)*

b) What advice will you give the lady even if all parameters are normal?

CHAPTER

5

ONCOLOGY

CERVICAL CA SCREENING

1. a) Describe methods of cervical carcinoma screening.
   b) Describe the etiopathogenesis of CA cervix and describe methods of prevention of CA cervix. *4+6 (Dec 2022)*

2. a) What are the current guidelines for cervical cancer screening?
   b) Outline the management of precancerous lesions of cervix. *5+5 (June 2021)*

3. a) Various modalities for screening of cancer cervix.
   b) HPV vaccine. *5+5 (June 2020)*

4. a) Liquid based cytology in cervical screening.
   b) Cervical screening guidelines. *5+5 (Dec 2019)*

5. a) What is the advantage of liquid base cytology? *2+4+4 (June 2018)*
   b) Pathogenesis of persistent HPV infection of cervix and its significance.
   c) How will you diagnose HPV infection and prevent it?

6. New guidelines for screening of carcinoma cervix? *4 (Dec 2016)*

7. Discuss the role of Pap smear and HPV testing for screening of cancer cervix. *5+5 (Dec 2014)*

8. a) What are the advantages of liquid base cytology over conventional Pap smear? *3+4+3 (June 2013)*
   b) Discuss the role of HPV DNA test in screening of cancer cervix.
   c) Describe the algorithmic approach to LSIL in a 35 year old woman.

COLPOSCOPY & CIN

9. 31-year-old with vaginal ulcer.
   a) Diagnostic tests. *4+2+4 (2025)*
   b) Treatment options for CIN1.
   c) Preventive measures for cervical cancer.

10. a) What is transformation zone? *2+4+4 (Oct 2024)*
    b) What are the changes seen on colposcopy in a suspected high grade intraepithelial neoplasia?

c) Describe the management of a case of CIN III on cervical biopsy.

11. Colposcopic assessment of cervical intraepithelial neoplasia:
    a) Enlist the 4 main features that need to be observed for the diagnosis of cervical intraepithelial neoplasia. *2+5+3 (June 2022)*
    b) How do these lesions appear in low grade CIN and high grade CIN after application of normal saline, 5% acetic acid solution and Lugol's iodine solution?
    c) What is Reid's colposcopy index? What is its significance?

12. a) Cervical intra-epithelial neoplasia. *5+5 (Dec 2018)*
    b) Screening methodology for early detection of cervical cancer.

13. a) What is the advantage of liquid base cytology? *2+4+4 (June 2018)*
    b) Pathogenesis of persistent HPV infection of cervix and its significance.
    c) How will you diagnose HPV infection and prevent it?

14. a) Newer methods of screening for premalignant lesions of cervix.
    b) Indications of colposcopy and its interpretations.
    c) Role of LEEP in pre-malignant lesion of cervix. *4+4+2 (June 2017)*

15. What is the role of colposcopy in management of vulval lesions? *3 (Dec 2018)*

HPV

16. HPV vaccine. *5 (June 2016)*

17. a) Mechanism of carcinogenesis by HPV in carcinoma cervix.
    b) What is the role of HPV detection in screening and follow up of cancer cervix? *4+ (4+2) (April 2016)*

18. a) Human papilloma virus vaccines. *5+5 (Dec 2015)*
    b) Treatment options for cervical intra-epithelial neoplasia (CIN).

19. HPV vaccine. *5 (June 2015)*

20. a) Describe the Human Papilloma Virus (HPV) infection and its mechanism of carcinogenesis.
    b) What is the natural history of HPV infections? *3+2+2+3 (Dec 2012)*
    c) How do you diagnose it?
    d) Write your comments on HPV vaccination.

CA CERVIX

21. a) Risk factors for cervical cancer. *2+3+5 (2025)*

b) Counseling 18-year-old on primary prevention.

c) Secondary preventive methods.

22.a) FIGO staging of carcinoma cervix.

b) Describe clinical presentation and management of carcinoma cervix stage 2B. *3+7 (Oct 2023)*

23.a) Discuss the preventive strategies for cancer cervix.

b) Describe the FIGO staging of cancer cervix. *6+4 (April 2023)*

24. How will you manage a case of 60 year lady with dirty foul smelling discharge with postcoital bleeding? *8 (June 2021)*

25.a) FIGO staging of cervical cancer. *2+2+2+4 (June 2019)*

b) What are the different modalities for staging of cervical cancers?

c) What are the prognostic factors for cervical cancers?

d) Management of stage IB of cervical cancer.

26. Radical trachelectomy for cervical cancer? *5+5 (Dec 2018)*

27.a) Enumerate the causes of post-coital bleeding? *2+4+4 (June 2016)*

b) How will you investigate and manage a 45 year old woman having post coital bleeding?

28.a) Risk factors of cancer cervix. *3+4+3 (June 2015)*

b) State FIGO staging of cervical cancer.

c) Therapeutic options in cervical intraepithelial neoplasia.

29.a) Define transformation zone. Discuss its evaluation. *3+3+4 (Dec 2013)*

b) What are the recent guidelines for screening for carcinoma cervix?

30.a) What is the lymphatic drainage of cervix and its surgical significance?

b) Describe clinical features of carcinoma cervix (stage IB) in a 30 years old woman.

c) What are the advantages of surgical management over radiotherapy or vice versa in such a case? *4+4+2 (June 2013)*

CA OVARY

31.a) Describe the recent FIGO staging of ovarian cancer.

b) Describe the pathogenesis of borderline ovarian tumor.

c) Discuss the management of a 30-year-old Para 2 detected post operatively as borderline mucinous ovarian tumor on histopathological examination after laparoscopic unilateral ovarian cystectomy done 2 weeks back for ovarian cyst. *3+4+3 (May 2024)*

32. Discuss role of genetic counselling and its effect on management of ovarian cancer. *10 (Dec 2022)*

33.a) What is meant by hormonally active ovarian tumour? Enlist various pathological types. *4+6 (June 2022)*
b) Diagnosis and management of oestrogen secreting ovarian tumours.

34.a) When will you suspect hereditary breast/ovarian cancer syndrome?
b) What are the strategies for prevention of hereditary ovarian cancer? *5+5 (June 2021)*

35.a) Latest FIGO classification of ovarian cancer. *5+5 (Dec 2020)*
b) How will you manage a case of a 56 year old woman with stage IIIc epithelial ovarian cancer?

36.a) Enumerate FIGO classification of carcinoma ovary.
b) Differential diagnosis of ovarian tumours. *5+5 (June 2020)*

37. Molecular biology of ovarian cancer and its clinical implications. *10 (June 2020)*

38.a) Give classification of benign ovarian neoplasm. *2+8 (June 2019)*
b) Diagnosis, complications and management of benign cystic teratoma.

39.a) Ovarian tumour marker. *5+5 (Dec 2018)*
b) Role of ovarian tumour marker in the management of ovarian cancer?

40.a) What are the risk factors for ovarian carcinoma? *2+2+6 (June 2018)*
b) Current evidence for screening of ovarian carcinoma?
c) Discuss the management principles of advanced ovarian carcinoma

41.a) What is chemoprophylaxis in ovarian cancer? *3+4+3 (April 2016)*
b) What is the role of bilateral salpingectomy?
c) What is the role of peritoneal stripping in peritoneal carcinoma?

42.a) Tumour markers for gynaecological cancers. *5+5 (June 2016)*
b) Intraperitoneal chemotherapy for treatment of ovarian cancer.

43.a) Preventive measures for epithelial ovarian cancer. *4+3+3 (Dec 2015)*
b) Place of fertility sparing surgery in ovarian malignancy.
c) Types of malignant germ cell ovarian tumours.

44.a) Hereditary breast and ovarian cancer. *5+5 (June 2015)*
b) Risk of Malignancy Index (RMI) for evaluation of ovarian masses.

45.a) What do you understand by adjuvant chemotherapy? *3+7 (Dec 2014)*
b) How will you manage a case of malignant epithelial ovarian tumour?

46.a) Describe familial ovarian cancer syndrome. *2+ (3+3) +2 (June 2014)*
b) What are proteomic and genomic approaches to its diagnosis?
c) What is the role of prophylactic oophorectomy?

47.a) What is the role of conservative surgery in gynaecological malignancy?
b) Write the fertility preserving surgical procedures and techniques for i) Ovarian and ii) cervical cancers. *2+4+4 (June 2014)*

48. Critically evaluate the role of neoadjuvant chemotherapy in ovarian malignancy. *4 (Dec 2016)*

GERM CELL OVARIAN TUMORS

49.a) Discuss the management of adnexal mass in pregnancy.
b) Discuss the management of malignant germ cell tumour in a 15 year old girl. *5+5 (April 2023)*

50.a) FIGO staging of carcinoma ovary. *5+5 (Dec 2019)*
b) Management of a 16 year old girl with a unilateral solid tumour in the ovary.

51. Management of ovarian malignancy in a 22 year old lady. *5 (Dec 2016)*

52.a) What are the causes of adnexal mass in an 18 year old unmarried girl?
b) How will you investigate her?
c) Outline the principles of management of germ cell tumour. *3+3+4 (June 2016)*

53.a) What are germ cell tumours of the ovary? *5+5 (April 2016)*
b) Outline the management of dysgerminoma.

54.a) Classify germ cell ovarian tumours? *4+ (3+3) (Dec 2014)*
b) Write in brief about lab & radiological findings and management of dysgerminoma.

55.a) What is the differential diagnosis of an adnexal mass in a young woman? *4+3+3 (June 2013)*
b) Describe the indications and follow up of fertility sparing surgery on a young woman with malignant ovarian tumour.

56. A 12 year old girl presents with unilateral adnexal mass.
a) Discuss its differential diagnosis. *3+3+4 (Dec 2012)*
b) Outline the investigation plan.
c) How will you manage a germ cell tumour in this girl?

57.a) Enumerate types of ovarian tumours seen in adolescent girl.
b) Describe the clinical characteristics of malignant ovarian tumours.

c) What are the tumours associated with ovarian malignancy?
3+4+3 (Dec 2011)

CA ENDOMETRIUM

58. 38-year-old with AUB & ET 16 mm.
    a) Differential diagnoses. 2+2+6 (June 2025)
    b) USG features of endometrial Ca.

34-year-old with atypical hyperplasia wanting fertility – management.

59.a) What is the latest FIGO 2023 staging for carcinoma endometrium?
   b) What are the high risk factors for carcinoma endometrium?
   c) Discuss the management of carcinoma endometrium FIGO stage 1A2.
4+2+4 (May 2024)

60. Discuss the management of case of endometrial intraepithelial neoplasia in a 35 year old nulliparous woman. 6 (April 2023)

61.a) Detail the recent FIGO staging of endometrial cancer.
   b) Describe the various prognostic factors and molecular markers in a case of endometrial cancer. 5+5 (June 2022)

62.a) Describe the FIGO classification of Endometrial carcinoma.
   b) Discuss how to evaluate the women for premalignant and malignant lesions of endometrium. 4+6 (June 2021)

63. Diagnosis and management of endometrial intraepithelial neoplasia.
5 (June 2020)

64. A 60 year old woman presents with post-menopausal bleeding.
    a) Discuss the differential diagnosis. 4+3+3 (Dec 2018)
    b) How will you investigate the patient?
    c) Outline the principles of management of endometrial carcinoma.

65.a) What are the causes of postmenopausal bleeding per vaginum in a 55 year old woman? 2+4+4 (June 2017)
   b) Give an approach to its diagnosis and its management?
   c) Current clinical guidelines in the management of stage I adenocarcinoma of body of uterus.

66.a) What is endometrial hyperplasia? 1+5+4 (June 2016)
   b) Classify endometrial hyperplasia, indicating their malignant potential.
   c) Outline the principles of management of atypical hyperplasia.

67. Role of chemotherapy in endometrial malignancy? 5 (June 2016)

68. Role of lymphadenectomy in the management of endometrial carcinoma. *5 (Dec 2015)*

69.a) How will you investigate a case of post-menopausal bleeding?
b) Give details of FIGO classification for endometrial carcinoma. *5+5 (Dec 2014)*

70. A 54 year old lady presents with postmenopausal bleeding.
a) How will you clinically evaluate her? *3+3+4 (Dec 2013)*
c) What investigations will you advise for her?
d) Outline the plan of management of endometrial carcinoma in her.

BREAST CA

71.a) List the aetiologies of galactorrhoea in non-lactating women.
b) Discuss the work up and various management options for a 32 year old parous lady with discharge from unilateral breast for 6 months. *4+6 (June 2022)*

VAGINAL CA

72.a) Describe the histological classification of vaginal intra-epithelial neoplasia (VaIN).
b) Discuss management options for VaIN. *4+6 (June 2022)*

73.a) Vaginal intra-epithelial neoplasia. *5+5 (Dec 2018)*
b) Sentinel node.

VULVAL CA

74. Write the causes and management of recurrent vulval ulcers. *10 (June 2021)*

75.a) Vulval intra epithelial neoplasia. *5+5 (Dec 2019)*
b) Management of lymph nodes in radical vulvectomy.

GTN

76.a) WHO classification of GTD. *2+4+4 (June 2025)*
b) Investigations & management of complete mole.
c) Placental site trophoblastic tumor.

77.a) Describe the types of gestational trophoblastic disease (GTD).
b) Describe the FIGO prognostic scoring system for gestational trophoblastic neoplasia (GTN) and chemotherapeutic options based on GTN score.

c) Detail the follow up and counselling of a case of hydatidiform mole at discharge from the facility following suction evacuation.

3+4+3 (May 2024)

78.a) Describe the classification of GTD and pathogenesis of gestational trophoblastic diseases.

b) Discuss management of patient with H. mole with coexisting live foetus at 14 weeks of gestation. 4+6 (Dec 2022)

79. A 38 years old Para 3 presents with history of irregular vaginal bleeding. She gives history of molar pregnancy 8 months ago. Her serum beta HCG is 12000 mIU/ml, uterus is normal size. USG shows theca lutein cyst 6 × 6 cm and chest X-ray shows 2 coin shaped lesions.

a) What is the FIGO staging and risk score of this case?

b) Discuss the management of this case. 3+7 (Dec 2021)

80.a) How is trophoblastic disease diagnosed? 5+5 (June 2020)

b) What is the management strategy of trophoblastic disease?

81.a) What are the histological categories of gestational trophoblastic neoplasia (GTN)? 2+4+4 (Dec 2016)

b) Work up a case of GTN.

c) Therapeutic option in low risk GTN.

82.a) Classification of Gestational trophoblastic neoplasia. 3+(3+4) (June 2015)

b) Staging of GTN and modified WHO prognostic scoring system.

83.a) What are the clinical features of Gestational Trophoblastic Neoplasia?

b) What is the WHO risk scoring in GTN?

c) Describe the single and multiagent chemotherapy in GTN and its follow up. 3+3+4 (June 2013)

TUMOR MARKERS

84.a) List the various tumour markers used in gynae oncology.

b) Describe the role of each tumour marker in diagnosis and prognosis of specific gynae cancers. 4+6 (May 2024)

85.a) Enumerate various tumour makers used in gynaecology.

b) Discuss the clinical significance of various tumour markers.

4+6 (Dec 2021)

OTHERS

86.a) What is sentinel node?

b) Discuss the role of Sentinel lymph node biopsy in the management of gynaecological cancers. *2+8 (June 2021)*

87. Role of PET-CT in gynaecology. *5 (Dec 2020)*

88. Role of various fertility preservation options available for cancer patients in females *5 (June 2015)*

89. Write briefly on:

a) PET-CT in gynaecological malignancy. *4+3+3 (June 2013)*

b) Chemo radiation in cervical malignancy.

c) Serum CA 125 as a tumour marker.

90.a) What is selective pelvic lymphadenectomy & its indications in relation to the gynaecological malignancy? *5+5 (June 2012)*

b) Describe the basis of concurrent chemo radiation and its application in gynaecological cancers.

CHAPTER

6

UROGYNECOLOGY

URINARY INCONTINENCE

1. a) Define stress urinary incontinence (SUI). *2+4+4 (Dec 2021)*
   b) Discuss the aetiology and evaluation of SUI.
   c) Critically appraise the vaginal procedures used in management of SUI.

2. a) What is the mechanism of bladder continence? *5+5 (June 2021)*
   b) Discuss the pharmacological management of overactive bladder.

3. a) Define stress urinary incontinence. Describe its aetiology and evaluation in brief.
   b) Management of a case of stress urinary incontinence in a 40 year old nulliparous female. *5+5 (Dec 2020)*

4. a) Physiology of female urinary continence *5+5 (Dec 2019)*
   b) Management of urinary retention in first trimester of pregnancy.

5. a) What is extra urethral incontinence? *2+2+6 (June 2019)*
   b) What are the causes of vesico vaginal fistula?
   c) Evaluation and management of vesico-vaginal fistula.

6. a) Discuss the disease spectrum and etio-pathology of pelvic floor dysfunction. *4+6 (June 2019)*
   b) Discuss pathophysiology, diagnosis and management of pelvic floor hypertonic disorders?

7. Management of genuine SUI. *5 (Dec 2018)*

8. Pathophysiology of urinary incontinence. *5 (June 2018)*

9. a) What are the risk factors and causes of SUI in mid-life?
   b) How will you confirm SUI?
   c) Current treatment of SUI. *2+4+4 (June 2017)*

10. a) Physiology of urinary incontinence. *4+3+3 (June 2015)*
    b) How will you evaluate incontinence in a 55 year old parous woman?
    c) How will you treat stress incontinence in such a woman?

11.a) What is stress incontinence? *2+2+2+4 (Dec 2013)*

b) Discuss the aetiology and evaluation.

c) Outline the plan of management of stress incontinence.

12.a) What is the physiological mechanism of urinary incontinence?

b) How will you investigate urge incontinence in a 55 year old parous woman?

c) What are the non-pharmacological and pharmacological approaches to treat urge incontinence? *3+4+3 (June 2013)*

13. Write the complications of sling surgery for SUI. *2 (June 2012)*

OVERACTIVE BLADDER

14. Discuss the pharmacological management of overactive bladder. *5 (June 2021)*

15. Medical management of overactive bladder. *5 (June 2018)*

16.a) Pharmacotherapy in overactive bladder. *3+4+3 (June 2017)*

b) Bio-feedback therapy in pelvic floor dysfunction.

c) Role of physiotherapy in post-natal women.

17.a) Describe the physiology of micturition. *3+2+5 (June 2014)*

b) What is the etio-pathogenesis of overactive bladder?

c) How do you diagnose and manage it?

URODYNAMIC STUDY

18. Urodynamic study. *5 (Dec 2018)*

19. List various parameters assessed on urodynamic study with their normal values. *3 (June 2012)*

PELVIC ORGAN PROLAPSE (POP)

20.a) Supports of uterus. *4+4+2 (June 2025)*

b) POP-Q classification of GU prolapse.

c) Aetiology of GU prolapse.

21. A 30-year-old P1LI woman presents with uterovaginal prolapse for the last 5 years. Her last childbirth was 5 years back and she is desirous of future fertility:

a) Discuss the nonsurgical options for this case. *4+6 (May 2024)*

b) Describe the various surgical options available for this case.

22.a) Describe delancey levels of pelvic support.

b) POP-Q classification.

c) Discuss the management of third degree uterovaginal prolapse in a 35 year old P2L2 woman. *3+3+4 (April 2023)*

23.a) Discuss the classification of pelvic organ prolapse.

b) Critically evaluate the treatment options available for a 26 years, para 2, with infravaginal elongation of cervix. *6+4 (Dec 2021)*

24.a) Pelvic organ prolapse quantification classification of female genital prolapse.

b) Discuss in brief management of vault prolapse. *5+5 (Dec 2020)*

25. POP-Q classification of uterovaginal prolapse. *5 (Dec 2019)*

26.a) Surgical anatomy of pelvic organ support. *5+5 (June 2017)*

b) Aetiology and surgical approach to nulliparous UV prolapse.

27.a) Role of mesh in pelvic organ prolapse. *5+3+2 (April 2016)*

b) Risks and benefits of mesh.

c) Classify types of mesh.

28.a) Outline the principles of preoperative evaluation to prevent post hysterectomy vaginal vault prolapse. *3+3+4 (Dec 2015)*

b) Measures taken during surgery to prevent it?

c) Surgical options available to treat vault prolapse.

29.a) What is POP-Q classification of pelvic organ prolapse?

b) Describe basic concept of site specific repair for genital prolapse.

c) Outline briefly preventive strategies for vault prolapse. *4+3+3 (June 2014)*

30.a) Describe the aetiology, classification and symptoms of prolapsed uterus. *2+2+2+4 (Dec 2013)*

b) Describe the management of vault prolapse in a 60 year old lady.

31.a) Describe the surgical anatomy of pelvic organ support system.

b) What are the etiological factors of POP in a 30 year old woman?

c) Describe basic principles of surgical correction of enterocele. *4+3+3 (June 2013)*

32.a) What is the preoperative preparation for major gynaecological surgery in utero-vaginal prolapse? *3+4+3 (June 2013)*

b) How will you counsel a woman before the surgical procedure for UV prolapse?

c) How will you manage bladder injury during cystocele repair?

33.a) What is the quantification system of pelvic organ prolapse (POP-Q)?

b) Compare it with conventional staging system.

c) Analyse critically its universal usage. *5+3+2 (Dec 2012)*

VAULT PROLAPSE

34. 52-year-old with vault prolapse.

a) Differential diagnosis. *2+2+6 (June 2025)*

b) Preventive measures at primary surgery.

c) Surgical options & describe one.

35. A 50 year old parous woman presents with vault prolapse, post vaginal hysterectomy done 5 years back for uterovaginal prolapse:

a) Describe the management options for the above case.

b) Discuss the strategies for prevention of vault prolapse during and after primary surgery. *6+4 (June 2022)*

36. Management of vault prolapse. *5 (Dec 2019)*

37.a) What is vaginal vault prolapse *2+4+4 (June 2018)*

b) Briefly describe the POP-Q staging of vault prolapse

c) What techniques you will perform during hysterectomy to prevent vault prolapse?

38.a) What are the techniques followed during hysterectomy to prevent vault prolapse? *4+6 (Dec 2016)*

b) Surgical procedure in a case of post-hysterectomy vault prolapse.

39.a) Outline the principles of preoperative evaluation to prevent post hysterectomy vaginal vault prolapse. *3+3+4 (Dec 2015)*

b) Measures taken during surgery to prevent it.

c) Surgical options available to treat vault prolapse.

FISTULA

40.a) Define vesicovaginal fistula (VVF). *2+5+3 (April 2023)*

b) How will you manage a case of VVF?

c) Discuss measures to prevent VVF in obstetrics.

41.a) How do you avoid ureteric injuries in endoscopic surgery?
b) Management of ureterovaginal fistula after hysterectomy.
05+5 (June 2020)

42.a) How will you avoid ureteric injuries at endoscopic surgery?
b) Management of ureterovaginal fistula after hysterectomy. 5+5 (Dec 2019)

43. On the 5th post-operative day after abdominal hysterectomy, the patient develops urinary leak per vaginum:
a) Institute management plan. 4+2+4 (Dec 2018)
b) List the factors that are associated with increased risk of urinary tract injuries?
c) Discuss steps for prevention of injury to urinary tract during hysterectomy.

44.a) Enumerate causes of genitourinary fistula. 2+6+2 (Dec 2016)
b) Outline the principles of management of a post hysterectomy fistula.
c) Enumerate complications of female sterilization.

45.a) Enumerate the causes of vesico-vaginal fistulae. 3+4+3 (April 2016)
b) Basic principles of its management.
c) Enumerate the treatment options for radiational fistulae.

46.a) Describe the preoperative evaluation on vesico-vaginal fistula.
b) What are the surgical principles of the management of post hysterectomy vesico-vaginal fistula?
c) Outline its post-operative management. 3+4+3 (June 2013)

CHAPTER

7

FAMILY PLANNING

BARRIER

1. a) What are barrier contraceptives?
   b) Discuss the benefits of using barrier contraceptives and what is the failure rate. *2+8 (June 2021)*

OCP

2. a) Discuss non contraceptive benefits of oral contraceptive pills in gynecology.
   b) How will you counsel and manage a 28-year-old parous woman with history of missed pills on day 10 of menses following use of OCP for 3 months? *6+4 (May 2024)*
3. A 19-year-old unmarried sexually active girl presented to adolescent clinic for contraceptive advice. Counsel her with appropriate contraceptive methods. *5 (Dec 2022)*
4. Missed pills. *5 (Dec 2020)*
5. a) What are the non-contraceptive benefits of OCP? *5+5 (Dec 2019)*
   b) Discuss the contraindications and side effects of the combined pill.
6. a) What are the clinical uses of combined oral contraceptives (COC)?
   b) What are the adverse effects of COC?
   c) Contraindications of COCs.
   d) COCs interactions with other drugs. *2+2+3+3 (June 2019)*
7. a) What are the advantages of newer generation oral contraceptive pills over conventional OCPs? *4+4+2 (June 2017)*
   b) Their relative and absolute contraindications?
   c) Missed pills. How to deal with it?
8. Enumerate non-contraceptive benefits of combined oral contraceptive pills. *3 (April 2016)*
9. a) Classify types of oral contraceptive pills available. *6+4 (June 2014)*
   b) What are their non-contraceptive benefits?

10.a) What are the routes of administration of hormonal contraception?

b) Describe vaginal-contraceptive ring its applications, advantages, and disadvantages.

c) Enumerate non contraceptive benefits of hormonal contraception.

3+4+3 (June 2013)

11. List the WHO eligibility criteria for combined pills, progestin only pills and intrauterine devices with the following special situations in women.

a) Known case of hypertension. 6+ (2+2) (June 2012)

b) Previous history of GDM.

c) Known case of epilepsy.

d) Patient of valvular RHD.

12.a) Define Pearl index. 2+4 (Dec 2011)

b) Describe the WHO medical eligibility criteria for the use of contraceptives and its clinical utility.

IUCD

13. Another patient requesting contraception was sexually active and is 46-year-old. Discuss her options. 5 (Dec 2022)

14.a) Discuss levonorgestrel intrauterine device – a boon in gynaecology.

b) Describe the management of a 28 year old parous woman with missing thread of Copper T IUCD following 2 months of insertion.

5+5 (June 2022)

15. a) A young newly married couple wants to postpone childbirth for three years. Describe various methods which can be advised to them with various advantages and disadvantages of different methods.

b) Discuss the types, indications and contraindications of long acting reversible contraception. 4+6 (Dec 2021)

16. How will you manage a case of misplaced CuT? 5 (Dec 2020)

17. Enumerate the contraindications and complications of intrauterine contraceptive devices. 10 (Dec 2020)

18.a) Enumerate the non-hormonal contraceptive methods.

b) Contraindications, mechanism of action, complications of intrauterine copper device. 5+5 (June 2020)

19. Long acting reversible contraceptives. 5 (June 2020)

20.a) What are the long acting reversible contraceptives (LARC)?

b) Methods, indications, contraindications, risks and side effects of LARC.

2+8 (June 2019)

21. Non-oral hormonal contraception. *4 (Dec 2016)*

22.a) Medical eligibility criteria for contraception. *4+6 (April 2016)*
   b) Non-oral hormonal contraception.

23.a) What are long acting reversible contraceptive methods (LARC)?
   b) As per WHO medical eligibility criteria, what are the absolute contraindications of hormonal contraceptives?
   c) Principles of tubal re-anastomosis. *3+3+4 (June 2016)*

24.a) Advantages of third generations intrauterine devices. *4+3+3 (Dec 2015)*
   b) Combined oral contraceptives and neoplasia)
   c) Contraceptive prescription for a woman with diabetic mellitus.

25.a) Various non-oral hormonal contraceptive methods. *6+4 (June 2015)*
   b) Non contraceptive uses of LNG-IUS.

26.a) Contraindications of use of intrauterine devices. *4+3+3 (June 2015)*
   b) What is the prognosis of pregnancy with retained intrauterine device?
   c) How will you evaluate a case of IUD user where thread is not visible?

27. Write short notes on:
   Postpartum IUCD. *5 (June 2014)*

28.a) What are the medical eligibility criteria of WHO for intrauterine contraceptive devices (IUCD)? *4+ (2+2+2) (Dec 2013)*
   b) Write the mechanism of action.
   c) Advantages and disadvantages of progesterone containing IUCD.

29. a) Government of India initiative on post placental IUCD (PP-IUCD) insertion. *4+3+3 (June 2012)*
   b) Frameless intrauterine devices.
   c) Association of pelvic inflammatory disease (PID) and intrauterine contraceptive devices (IUCD).

30.a) What are the various types of IUCDs prevalent in India?
   b) What are the contraindications for its use as per medical eligibility criteria?
   c) What are the non-contraceptive uses and benefits of hormone releasing IUCDs? *4+3+3 (Dec 2012)*

PROGESTERONE & INJECTABLE CONTRACEPTIVES

31.a) Injectable hormonal contraceptives & application.
   b) Medical eligibility. *3+4 (June 2025)*

Implants

32. Implants as contraceptives. *3 (June 2025)*

33. Critically evaluate WHO Medical eligibility criteria for injection medroxy progesterone acetate as a contraceptive. *10 (June 2021)*

34. Antra (Injectable contraceptive MPA). *5 (Dec 2020)*

35. WHO medical eligibility criteria for progesterone only pills. *5 (Dec 2020)*

36. Advantages and disadvantages of newer progestins. *3 (Dec 2016)*

37. Write short notes on:
    Combined injectable contraceptives. *5 (June 2014)*

TRANSDERMAL PATCHES

38. Write about transdermal contraceptive patch. *3 (Dec 2021)*

EMERGENCY CONTRACEPTION

39. Emergency contraception. *5 (June 2020)*

40.a) Define emergency contraception. *2+4+4 (Dec 2013)*
   b) Describe the various methods available.
   c) Discuss their mode of action and failure rates.

41.a) What are the various methods of emergency contraception?
   b) Mention their mode of action.
   c) Enumerate their side effects and failure rates.
   d) Write your opinion on over-the-counter (OTC) availability of emergency contraceptives. *3+2+2+3 (Dec 2012)*

42. Critically evaluate the different methods of emergency contraception. *4 (Dec 2011)*

SERM (ORMELOXIFENE/CENTCHROMAN)

43.a) Discuss the purpose of WHOs medical eligibility criteria (MEC) for contraceptive use and explain the concept of MEC wheel.
   b) Describe the usage, indications, advantages and disadvantages of "Antara" and "Chhaya" available in India under the basket of contraception. *4+6 (May 2024)*

44.a) Discuss the indication, contraindications, side effects and mechanism of action of Ormeloxifene. *5+5 (April 2023)*

b) What contraception you will advise to a recently delivered woman?

45. Describe the usage, indications, advantages and disadvantages of centchroman. *5 (June 2022)*

STERILIZATION

46.a) Discuss the role of opportunistic salpingectomy during benign gynecological surgery. *2+6+2 (May 2024)*

b) Describe various methods for tubal sterilization. Discuss the advantages and disadvantages of each.

c) List the eligibility criteria for tubal ligation.

47. Interval sterilisation. *5 (April 2023)*

48. Discuss the various techniques of female sterilization. *10 (Dec 2020)*

49.a) What are the standards of female sterilization?

b) What are the different techniques of tubal ligation? *5+5 (June 2020)*

50.a) Describe in brief different modalities of tubal ligation. *5+5 (June 2018)*

b) What is the eligibility criteria for female sterilization with caesarean section as per Government of India?

51.a) Enumerate different methods and timings of female tubal ligation.

b) Their eligibility criterion and preoperative assessment?

c) Female sterilization indemnity bond scheme. *4+4+2 (June 2017)*

52.a) What are the advantages of laparoscopic sterilization?

b) Long term risks of tubal ligation.

c) Health benefits of tubal sterilization. *3+4+3 (April 2016)*

53.a) Different methods of female sterilization. *3+3+4 (Dec 2015)*

b) Enumerate the risks of tubal sterilization.

c) Reasons for failure of tubal sterilization.

54.a) What are the different methods of female sterilization? *6+4 (Dec 2014)*

b) Discuss the process of consent for tubectomy.

55.a) What are the indications for tubal recanalization? *3+7 (Dec 2014)*

b) Describe factors which improve success of recanalization.

VASECTOMY

56. Non scalpel vasectomy. *5 (April 2023)*

57. Male sterilization is easier and safer than female sterilization.
   a) Justify this statement. *5+2+3 (Dec 2018)*
   b) What is NSV?
   c) What are the important points that you would like to discuss with a couple choosing vasectomy?

58.a) What are the recent developments in male contraception?
   b) RISUG or reversible inhibition of sperms under guidance.
   c) Non scalpel vasectomy: Technique. *4+2+4 (Dec 2016)*

59.a) Contraceptive prescription for a seropositive woman.
   b) Risk of vasectomy.
   c) Essure. *3+4+3 (Dec 2015)*

POSTPARTUM CONTRACEPTION

60. Describe various contraceptive choices for postpartum women with heart disease. *2 (May 2024)*

61. Describe post-partum contraception. *4 (Dec 2021)*

62. Postpartum contraception. *5 (Dec 2020)*

63.a) What are the contraceptives available today in the basket of choices under the National Family Planning Programme of India?
   b) Postpartum contraception. *3+7 (Dec 2018)*

64. Post-partum contraception. *10 (Dec 2014)*

MISCELLANEOUS

65. Describe components of Family Planning Indemnity Scheme (FPIS). *5 (June 2022)*

66.a) What are the adolescent health programmes in India and their current status?
   b) Need and methods of adolescent contraception. *5+5 (June 2017)*

67.a) Describe female condom. *3+4+3 (Dec 2014)*
   b) How to use it and its advantages?

CHAPTER

8

MEDICAL TERMINATION OF PREGNANCY (MTP)

1. a) First trimester MTP. *5 (Dec 2020)*

2. a) MTP Act. *4+6 (June 2019)*
   b) Management of septic abortion.

3. a) Describe methods for second trimester termination of pregnancy.
   b) A case of MTP at 18 weeks pregnancy received Mifepristone and Misoprostol according to protocol with no result. Discuss reasons of failure and management of the case. *5+5 (June 2018)*

4. a) What is cafeteria approach and counselling for post abortal contraception? *5+5 (June 2017)*
   b) Timing of initiation, advantages and disadvantages.

5. Amendments to original MTP Act. *5 (Dec 2016)*

6. a) What is medical termination of pregnancy (MTP) Act 1971?
   b) What are the indications for termination of pregnancy under this Act?
   c) What are the various methods of termination of pregnancy in first trimester? *4+2+4 (Dec 2013)*

7. a) What are the methods used for first trimester MTP?
   b) Write the advantages and disadvantages of medical methods of abortion?
   c) Complications of manual vacuum aspiration. *2+(3+3) +2 (Dec 2012)*

CHAPTER

9

OBSTETRICS

GESTATIONAL DIABETES IN PREGNANCY (GDM)

1. a) Define criteria for diagnosis of polyhydramnios and enumerate its various etiologies. *4+4+2 (May 2024)*
   b) Discuss the management of a primigravida with 28 weeks pregnancy and gestational diabetes mellitus.
   c) Describe the complications in a large for date baby born to a diabetic mother.

2. a) Discuss antenatal, intrapartum and postanatal management of a patient with gestational diabetes. *5+5 (Oct 2023)*
   b) Enumerate the fetal and maternal complications in patients with diabetes mellitus.

3. a) Discuss the carbohydrate metabolism in pregnancy. *3+4+3 (April 2023)*
   b) Describe the various screening methods for gestational diabetes.
   c) Role of oral hypoglycemics in GDM.

4. a) Enumerate the changes in carbohydrate metabolism during pregnancy.
   b) How will you manage a case of overt diabetes mellitus during pregnancy? *5+5 (Dec 2020)*

5. a) Discuss the different screening methods for gestational diabetes.
   b) Describe the neonatal complications in infants of diabetic mothers. *2+8 (Dec 2019)*

6. A 33 year woman with Type 2 Diabetes on OHA presents for ANC at 6 weeks pregnancy. *3+4+3 (Dec 2018)*
   a) What is the present evidence regarding the use of OHA in pregnancy?
   b) Outline the antenatal monitoring of hyperglycaemia and management plan of this lady?

7. a) Methods for screening for gestational diabetes in pregnancy.
   b) Complications of hyperglycaemia on pregnancy and foetus. *4+ (3+3) (June 2016)*

8. a) Outline the management of diabetes mellitus in pregnancy. *3+4+3 (April 2016)*
   b) How would you manage shoulder dystocia in macrosomic foetus?

9. a) Screening protocols for GDM. *4+3+3 (Dec 2015)*
   b) Role of hypoglycaemic agents in the management of GDM.
   c) Management of diabetic ketoacidosis.

10. a) Define GDM. *2+8 (Dec 2014)*
    b) Discuss different screening protocols for GDM.

11. a) Describe carbohydrate metabolism in Gestational Diabetes Mellitus (GDM). *3+3+4 (June 2013)*
    b) How will you screen high and low risk pregnant woman for GDM?
    c) Enumerate the steps to achieve optimal glycaemic control in GDM.

HYPERTENSION

12. a) Classify HDP (Hypertensive disorders of pregnancy). *3+4+3(June 2025)*
    b) Bundle approach for hypertensive emergencies.
    c) Management of status eclampticus refractory to $MgSO_4$.

13. a) Describe the changes in the vascular architecture of uterus and endometrium in pregnancy. *4+2+4 (Oct 2024)*
    b) Discuss the abnormal vascular changes seen in cases with pre-eclampsia.
    c) Enumerate 4 important risk factors for development of pre-eclampsia.

14. a) Describe various screening tests for preeclampsia in early pregnancy.
    b) How will you manage a case of pulmonary edema with severe preeclampsia presented with BP of 180/120 mmHg at admission?
    c) Describe the management of eclampsia at 34 weeks period of gestation in a primigravida. *3+3+4 (May 2024)*

15. Management of eclampsia. *5 (Oct 2023)*

16. a) Describe the etiopathogenesis of pre-eclampsia. *4+3+3 (April 2023)*
    b) Biomarkers in pre-eclampsia.
    c) What are the preventive measures for pre-eclampsia?

17. a) Describe pathophysiology of preeclampsia in pregnancy and its classification.
    b) Describe the various systemic complications of preeclampsia based on its pathophysiology. *4+6 (June 2022)*

18. a) Define preeclampsia. *3+7 (Dec 2020)*
    b) How will you manage a case of Primigravida at 34 weeks with eclampsia?

19.a) How will you classify and define hypertensive disorders of pregnancy?
b) Role of anti-hypertensives in preeclampsia. *5+5 (Dec 2019)*

20.a) Pathogenesis of pre-eclampsia. *5+5 (Dec 2018)*
b) Complications of pre-eclampsia and its prevention.

21. HELLP syndrome: its differential diagnosis and management. *5 (June 2017)*

22.a) Enumerate the causes of convulsions during pregnancy.
b) What are the maternal and foetal risks of eclampsia?
c) How will you manage a G1P0 admitted at 32 weeks of pregnancy with eclampsia? *2+ (2+2) +4 (June 2016)*

23. A woman with 7 months of pregnancy has a blood pressure of 140/100 mmHg. *2+ (4+4) (June 2015)*
a) What is her diagnosis?
b) What investigations would you like to do and how would you manage this patient?

24.a) Enumerate the causes of generalised oedema in a primi-gravida with term pregnancy. *3+3+4 (June 2013)*
b) Describe the features of severe preeclampsia.
c) How will you prevent eclampsia in pregnant woman with severe pre-eclampsia?

MULTIPLE PREGNANCY

25.a) Criteria for sFGR in monochorionic twins. *2+3+5 (June 2025)*
b) Stages of sFGR.
c) Compare expectant vs interventions.

26. Placental anastomosis in MC gestations. *5 (June 2025)*

27.a) What is the mechanism of twinning?
b) How will you manage a dichorionic diamniotic twin pregnancy at 32 weeks pregnancy with discordant growth? *5+5 (Oct 2024)*

28.a) Describe the criteria for diagnosis of discordant twins. Discuss its pathophysiology.
b) Discuss the various complications of monochorionic twin pregnancy and outline management of each. *2+4 (May 2024)*

29.a) Discuss antenatal management in multifetal gestation.
b) Enumerate indications, procedure and complications of fetal reduction treatment. *6+4 (Oct 2023)*

30. Discuss the staging of twin-twin transfusion syndrome and management options. *5 (April 2023)*

31. a) Enumerate the antepartum complications of twin pregnancy.
    b) Describe the management of single fetal demise in monochorionic twin pregnancy at 32 weeks of gestation.
    c) Discuss the intrapartum complications of twins. *3+3+4 (April 2023)*

32. a) Explain the genesis of twin-twin transfusion syndrome (TTTS).
    b) How to diagnose a case of TTTS?
    c) Describe the management of a case of TTTS at 24 weeks of gestation in primigravida with twin pregnancy. *2+4+4 (June 2022)*

33. a) Explain the genesis of Twin Gestation. *5+5 (June 2021)*
    b) What are the complications of monochorionic twin pregnancy?

34. a) Quintero staging system of twin-to-twin transfusion syndrome (TTTS).
    b) Latest management of TTTS. *6+4 (June 2020)*

35. a) What are the different methods to assess the chorionicity in pregnancy?
    b) What are the implications of chorionicity in management of twin pregnancy? *5+5 (June 2020)*

36. a) What are the different methods to assess chorionicity in pregnancy?
    b) Discuss the various implications of chorionicity in management of a twin pregnancy. *5+5 (Dec 2019)*

37. a) What are the different antenatal complications of twin pregnancy?
    b) Assessment and management after delivery of first baby.
    c) Management of triple pregnancy. *3+3+4 (Dec 2018)*

38. A patient aged 39 years with triplet pregnancy reports to you at 6weeks gestation conceived after in vitro fertilization.
    a) What will be your salient points for counselling in this scenario in reference to ANC management in first trimester and aneuploidy screening?
    b) What are the complications of multiple pregnancy?
    c) How will you monitor feto-maternal wellbeing in a pregnant woman with multiple pregnancy antenatally? *4+2+4 (June 2018)*

39. a) Enlist foetal risks in twin gestation. *3+4+3 (June 2017)*
    b) How and when will you establish chorionicity of twin pregnancy?
    c) How will you diagnose and manage twin to twin transfusion syndrome?

40. Enumerate complications and management of a monochorionic twin pregnancy. *5 (Dec 2016)*

41.a) Enumerate the factors that influence the increased incidence of twinning. 2+2+6 (June 2016)

b) How would you determine the chorionicity and amnionicity.

42.a) What is TTS? 2+4+4 (April 2016)

b) What are the stages of TTS?

c) Management and prognosis of TTS.

d) Management of discordant twins.

43.a) What is multifetal pregnancy reduction? 2+ (2+4+2) (April 2016)

b) Its purpose, technique and precautions?

44. Twin reversed arterial perfusion. 5 (Dec 2015)

45.a) What do you understand by zygosity and chorionicity of twin pregnancy?

b) How will you manage a case of monoamniotic, monochorionic twin pregnancy? 3+4 (Dec 2014)

CARDIAC

46.a) Cardiovascular/hemodynamic changes near term. 4+4+2 (June 2025)

b) Precautions in RHD with severe mitral stenosis at 32 weeks.

c) Supine hypotension syndrome.

47.a) Describe the physiological changes in cardiovascular system during pregnancy. 4+2+4 (April 2023)

b) Enumerate the causes of breathlessness in pregnancy.

c) Discuss the management of primigravida with 28 weeks pregnancy with mitral stenosis.

48. What is the basis of WHO risk classification of heart disease in pregnancy? Discuss management of a 23 years old primi gravida with 20 weeks of amenorrhea diagnosed with rHD with mitral stenosis, history of mitral mechanical valve replacement 3 years back with NYHA class 3 functional status now. 5+5 (Dec 2022)

49.a) What is preconception counselling? 2+8 (June 2021)

b) How will you do pre conceptional counselling in 24 year 24-year-old nulliparous woman with rheumatic heart disease with mitral stenosis?

50.a) Cardiovascular changes during pregnancy. 4+2+4 (June 2018)

b) What are the clinical indicators of heart disease in pregnancy?

c) How will you manage a case of severe mitral stenosis reported to you in second trimester of pregnancy?

51.a) What are the physiological cardiovascular adaptations in pregnancy?
b) How will you diagnose cardiac disease in pregnancy?
c) Management of pregnant women with prosthetic mitral valve.
3+3+4 (June 2017)

52. Peripartum cardiomyopathy: Diagnosis and management. 5 (June 2016)

53.a) How does the presence of mitral stenosis impact the pregnant patient?
b) What are the indications for correction during pregnancy for this condition?
c) How will you manage a patient after mitral valvuloplasty done in fifth month of pregnancy? 3+2+5 (June 2016)

54.a) Classify functional heart disease? 4+4+2 (April 2016)
b) How would you manage labour in women with rheumatic heart disease?
c) Role of anticoagulants in patients with prosthetic valve in pregnancy?

55.a) Haemodynamic changes in pregnancy. 4+3+3 (June 2015)
b) Effect of mitral stenosis on pregnancy.
c) Preventive measures to be taken to avoid complications in pregnant women with mitral stenosis.

56. Which anticoagulant, when and why to be used in a pregnant woman with prosthetic heart valve? 4+3+3 (Dec 2014)

57. A 20 year old G1P0 with 14 weeks pregnancy is diagnosed to be having RHD with mitral stenosis. 4+3+3 (June 2014)
How would you monitor her during pregnancy, childbirth and postpartum?

58.a) Enumerate clinical indicators of heart disease during pregnancy?
b) What is NYHA classification of heart disease and its prognostication?
c) Give contraceptive advice for a woman with mitral stenosis going on discharge after delivery. 3+3+4 (June 2012)

IUGR

59.a) Diagnostic criteria for early FGR. 4+4+2 (June 2025)
b) Surveillance & management for Stage 1 FGR at 28 weeks.
c) Timing of birth in late FGR.

60.a) Define small for gestation age (SGA) and its various aetiologies.
b) Discuss the work up and management of a pregnant woman with suspected foetal growth restriction at 28 weeks of gestation.
4+6 (June 2022)

61.a) Define foetal growth restriction. 1+3+6 (Dec 2016)
b) Enumerate the causes of FGR.
c) How will you manage a case of FGR at 32 weeks?

62.a) Problems of SGA foetus. 2+4+4 (June 2015)
b) Various techniques for evaluation of relative risks to SGA foetus.
c) Evidence based guidelines for management of such a case.

63.a) What is IUGR pregnancy? 3+7 (Dec 2014)
b) Discuss foetal surveillance during antenatal period.

64.a) Define intrauterine growth restriction. 2+4+4 (June 2013)
b) What is the role of Doppler flow studies in the management of IUGR?
c) Describe the perinatal problems of IUGR babies.

RH ISOIMMUNISATION

65.a) Describe etiopathogenesis of Rh isoimmunization of pregnancy.
b) Discuss the management of a case of Rh immunized pregnancy of gravida 3 para 1, living issue 1 at 30 weeks period of gestation with previous one intrauterine death. 4+6 (May 2024)

66.a) Enumerate causes of foetal hydrops. 3+7 (Dec 2022)
b) Discuss diagnosis and management of immune foetal hydrops at 22 weeks' gestation.

67.a) What is meant by Rh isoimmunised pregnancy? 2+6+2 (June 2022)
b) Discuss the management options gravid 2 para 1 Rh isoimmunised pregnancy at 30 weeks period of gestation.
c) Describe management of Rh isoimmunised neonate.

68.a) What are the causes of feto-maternal haemorrhage? 3+4+3 (June 2021)
b) How would you measure feto-maternal haemorrhage?
c) Discuss the use of Routine Antenatal Anti-D Prophylaxis (RAADP) with dose.

69.a) What is feto-maternal haemorrhage? How does it affect an Rh negative woman? 4+2+4 (June 2016)
b) Enumerate the causes of feto maternal haemorrhage.
c) How would you calculate the dose of anti-D required to prevent Rh iso-immunisation?

70.a) What are the non-invasive and invasive techniques to identify foetal isoimmunisation in Rh negative pregnancy? 5+5 (June 2017)
b) Role of intra-uterine foetal blood transfusion.

71.a) What do you understand by Rh incompatibility? *4+(3+3) (Dec 2014)*

b) Discuss its management during antenatal period and labour and delivery in a primigravida Rh negative woman.

72.a) Enumerate the causes of hydrops fetalis. Describe its pathophysiology.

b) How would you manage a Rh negative pregnant woman diagnosed with hydrops fetalis at 32 weeks of pregnancy? *3+3+4 (Dec 2013)*

ANAEMIA

73. a) Describe the classifications of anemia based on its type and severity.

b) Discuss the workup and management of a case of severe anemia at 30 weeks period of gestation and its complications. *2+6 (May 2024)*

74.a) Discuss iron metabolism in pregnancy. *5+5 (Oct 2023)*

b) Describe management of second gravid with Hb 8gm% at 32 weeks of gestation.

75.a) Classify anaemia in pregnancy. *2+3+5 (April 2023)*

b) What tests should be done to detect thalassemia in mother?

c) Discuss the management of a woman with severe anaemia at 34 weeks pregnancy.

76.a) Describe the role of ferric carboxymaltose in treatment of anaemia in pregnancy and postpartum. *2+4+4 (June 2022)*

b) How to differentiate between different types of microcytic anaemia in pregnant women and treatment for each type of microcytic anaemia?

c) Describe the complications of anaemia in pregnancy.

77. A multigravida with haemoglobin of 6 g% had no antenatal care till 30 weeks of pregnancy. How will you investigate and manage this case? *5+5 (June 2015)*

78. How will you investigate and manage a case of severe anaemia at 32 weeks of gestation? *5+5 (Dec 2014)*

79.a) A primigravida is diagnosed with severe anaemia (Hb 3g%) at 36 weeks of gestation. Enumerate various maternal and foetal complications of severe anaemia. *2+4+4 (Dec 2013*

b) How will you investigate and mange her?

THALASSEMIA IN PREGNANCY

80.a) What tests should be done to detect thalassemia in mother?

b) Discuss the management of a woman with severe anaemia at 34 weeks pregnancy. *3+5 (April 2023)*

81.a) What are the current recommendations and methods for screening for thalassemia in pregnancy? *5+5 (June 2017)*

b) Management of pregnant women with thalassemia trait.

82.a) What is thalassemia? *3+ (3+4) (Dec 2014)*

b) How will you investigate and mange a pregnancy where both parents are thalassemic carriers?

THROMBOCYTOPENIA IN PREGNANCY

83.a) Define thrombocytopenia in pregnancy. *2+3+5 (June 2022)*

b) Write the etiologic classification of thrombocytopenia in pregnancy.

c) Diagnosis and management considerations for 'Gestational thrombocytopenia'.

84.a) What are the causes of thrombocytopenia in pregnancy?

b) How will you evaluate such a case?

c) What is the management of a case of ITP in pregnancy? *5+2+3 (June 2014)*

JAUNDICE/IHC

85.a) Discuss the diagnosis, prognostication and management of a case of cholestasis of pregnancy. *6+4 (May 2024)*

b) Discuss the workup of a case to differentiate between various etiologies of jaundice in pregnancy.

86.a) Describe pathophysiology of intrahepatic cholestatsis of pregnancy (IHCP) and its implications on fetomaternal outcome. *6+4 (Oct 2023)*

b) Enumerate current recommendations for management of IHCP.

87. Discuss the management of a primigravida with 32 weeks pregnancy with acute fatty liver of pregnancy. *5 (April 2023)*

88. Discuss the basis and management of IHPC. *5 (Dec 2022)*

89.a) Describe etiopathogenesis of cholestasis of pregnancy and its various complications. *6+4 (June 2022)*

b) Discuss the various aetiologies of jaundice in pregnancy.

90.a) Define cholestasis of pregnancy. *2+3+5 (June 2021)*

b) How is obstetric cholestasis diagnosed?

c) Outline the management of intrahepatic cholestasis of pregnancy at 28 weeks of gestation in a Primigravida.

91.a) Etiopathology of acute fatty liver disease in pregnancy. *4+6 (June 2020)*
b) How will you manage such a case?

92.a) Acute fatty liver of pregnancy. *5+5 (Dec 2019)*
b) How do you differentiate it from viral hepatitis?

93.a) Causes of jaundice during pregnancy. *2+8 (June 2019)*
b) Diagnosis and management of viral hepatitis during pregnancy.

94.a) What is the differential diagnosis of jaundice in pregnancy?
b) Write the diagnostic for each of the above.
c) How will you manage a case of acute fatty liver of pregnancy at 34 weeks of pregnancy? *2+4+4 (Dec 2016)*

95. Pathogenesis and management of intra hepatic cholestasis of pregnancy. *4+6 (April 2016)*

96.a) What are the causes of jaundice in pregnancy? *3+4+3 (June 2013)*
b) How will you investigate and mange a case of intrahepatic cholestasis (IHC)?
c) What are the foetal complications of IHC?

HbsAg POSITIVE PREGNANCY

97. A HbsAg positive patient admitted at 36 weeks of gestation in the obstetrical ward.
a) What precautions you will observe to avoid transmission to health care provider? *5+5 (June 2018)*
b) How will you prevent perinatal transmission to the neonate?

98.a) Why is pregnancy considered high risk for HbsAg positive women?
b) How will you manage such a woman in labour?
c) Management of her new-born. *2+4+4 (June 2016)*

RENAL DISORDERS

99.a) Discuss the etiopathogenesis of pyelonephritis in pregnancy.
b) Discuss its diagnosis, management and complications in pregnancy. *2+8 (Dec 2022)*

100.a) Discuss the renal physiology in pregnancy. *5+5 (June 2021)*
b) Write about the pathogenesis of Acute Kidney Injury (AKI).

101.a) Define asymptomatic bacteriuria.
b) Management of acute renal failure in pregnancy. *4+3 (Dec 2020)*

102. Diagnosis, complications and management of a case of acute pyelonephritis during pregnancy? *3 (Dec 2016)*

103.a) What are the pregnancy induced urinary tract changes?
b) What is asymptomatic bacteriuria & its impact on pregnancy?
c) How will you manage acute pyelonephritis in pregnancy? *3+4+3 (April 2016)*

104.a) Enumerate the maternal and foetal complications during pregnancy in a woman who has had a renal transplant. *5+3+2 (April 2016)*
b) How will you monitor this pregnancy?
c) Outline a delivery plan for this woman.

105.a) What are the physiological and anatomical changes in the urinary system during pregnancy? *3+2+2+3 (Dec 2013)*
b) Define asymptomatic bacteriuria.
c) How does it affect the pregnancy?
d) Write the management of asymptomatic bacteriuria.

106.a) Describe the physiological changes in the renal functions during normal pregnancy. *3+3+4 (Dec 2012)*
b) Enumerate the causes of acute renal failure (ARF) during pregnancy.
c) Outline the management of ARF during pregnancy.

OBESITY

107. A 32 year primigravida 120 kg (BMI 38 kg/m^2) presents at 6 weeks of pregnancy. There is no other significant medical history. *5+5 (Dec 2018)*
a) Likely antepartum and intra-partum complications of the above case.
b) Peri-operative management in case she undergoes a LSCS.

108. A morbidly obese 30 years old patient approaches for pre-pregnancy counselling before bariatric surgery.
a) What will you counsel the patient *5+5 (June 2018)*
b) What are the complications during pregnancy in such a patient?

109.a) How will you counsel a young low risk primigravida regarding dietary intake? *5+2+3 (Dec 2016)*
b) How does obesity affect pregnancy?
c) Obstetric management of a pregnant patient with prior history of bariatric surgery.

THYROID PROBLEMS IN PREGNANCY

110.a) Discuss thyroid metabolism in pregnancy. *5+5 (Oct 2023)*
b) Discuss in detail management of thyroid dysfunction in pregnancy

111. Post-partum thyroiditis: Diagnosis and management. 5 (June 2017)

112. Management of hypothyroidism in pregnancy. 5 (June 2015)

113. a) Describe the physiological changes of thyroid during pregnancy.
   b) What are the maternal and fetal complications of hypothyroidism?
   c) Discuss the management of a pregnant woman with overt hypothyroidism. 3+3+4 (Dec 2013)

ASTHMA

114. a) Enumerate the causes of dyspnoea in pregnancy. 2+3+5 (June 2012)
   b) Describe in brief the effects of bronchial asthma on pregnancy and vice versa.
   c) How will you manage a case of asthma during labour?

EPILEPSY IN PREGNANCY

115. a) What are the course of epilepsy in pregnancy? 4+6 (June 2020)
   b) Discuss the common drugs used in pregnancy with epilepsy.

116. a) Enumerate the causes of convulsions during pregnancy.
   b) How does epilepsy affect pregnancy?
   c) Outline the principles of management during pregnancy. 3+3+4 (Dec 2013)

117. A known case of epilepsy wishes to plan for pregnancy.
   a) How will you counsel her? 2+3+3+2 (Dec 2012)
   b) What are the effects of epilepsy on pregnancy?
   c) Mention the effects of antiepileptic drugs on pregnancy.
   d) Outline your proposed plan for managing her during labour.

SKIN CHANGES IN PREGNANCY

118. a) Define physiological skin changes during pregnancy. 2+3+5 (Dec 2022)
   b) Enumerate aetiology of pruritis in pregnancy.
   c) Discuss the basis and management of IHPC.

APH (PLACENTA PREVIA)

119. a) Describe risk factors for placenta accreta. 5+5 (Oct 2023)
   b) Discuss management of G2P1 post LSCS pregnancy at 34 weeks suspected to have placenta accreta on routine ultrasound examination.

120.a) Define antepartum haemorrhage (APH). *1+2+7 (April 2023)*

b) Enumerate the causes of APH.

c) Discuss the management of a primigravida with APH at 32 weeks gestation.

121.a) Describe the Nitabuch's layer. *1+4+5 (Dec 2022)*

b) Describe the diagnosis of PAS (Placenta Accreta Spectrum).

c) Discuss management of placenta increta at 36 weeks.

122.a) What is Placenta Accreta Syndrome (PAS)? *2+2+3+3 (June 2020)*

b) What are risk factors for PAS?

c) How will you diagnose it?

d) Management of PAS.

123.a) Placenta accreta and its diagnosis by imaging.

b) Management of a previous caesarean with suspected placenta accreta.

124. A multigravida with previous LSCS is found to have anterior type 3 placenta previa on her 28 weeks scan. *3+3+4 (Dec 2018)*

a) Antenatal management of this patient.

b) Enumerate the anticipated problems during LSCS in this patient.

c) Enumerate the options of management if morbidly adherent placenta is encountered in this patient.

125. Diagnosis and management of morbidly adherent placenta. *5+5 (Dec 2016)*

126.a) What are the various types of morbid adhesions of placenta?

b) Diagnostic modalities and management options for morbid adhesions of placenta. *2+ (4+4) (April 2016)*

127. Important issues in the surgical management of placenta previa accreta. *5 (Dec 2015)*

128.a) Classify Placenta previa. *3+2+5 (June 2014)*

b) What are the causes of placenta previa?

c) How will you confirm its diagnosis?

d) What are the problems in its management?

129.a) Define and classify morbidly adherent placenta (MAP).

b) What is the role of ultrasound and MRI in diagnosis of MAP?

c) What are the complications of MAP and how will you manage them? *2+4+4 (Dec 2013)*

APH (ABRUPTIO PLACENTA)

130.a) Define placenta accreta spectrum. *2+4+4 (June 2025)*
b) USG features.
c) Management of placenta percreta at 32 weeks.

131. Management of undiagnosed placenta increta in emergency CS. *4 (June 2025)*

132.a) Enumerate the aetiology of abruptio placentae. *4+6 (June 2020)*
b) How will you manage a case of abruptio placentae? *5+5 (Dec 2019)*

133.a) Mention the predisposing factors for abruptio placenta.
b) What is Couvelaire uterus?
c) Management of abruptio placenta. *2+2+6 (June 2019)*

134.a) What are the predisposing factors of abruption placenta?
b) How will you diagnose it?
c) What are its complications?
d) How will you manage a G3P2L2 admitted at 38 week with the diagnosis of abruption placenta? *2+2+2+4 (Dec 2013)*

DVT

135.a) Enumerate various risk factors for postpartum venous thrombosis.
b) Discuss the diagnosis and management of a case of postpartum deep vein thrombosis of unilateral leg at day 7 of caesarean section. *4+6 (May 2024)*

136.a) Why pregnancy is considered a hypercoagulable state?
b) What are the risk factors for venous thromboembolism in pregnancy and puerperium?
c) Discuss thromboprophylaxis in pregnancy. *3+4+3 (June 2021)*

137.a) Pregnancy is a thrombogenic condition. Justify this statement.
b) What is the role of thromboprophylaxis in a postnatal patient? *5+5 (Dec 2020)*

138.a) What are the risk factors of venous thromboembolism in obstetric and gynaecological practice? *2+4+4 (June 2018)*
b) How will you prevent VTE in your clinical practice?
c) How will you suspect and mange a case of pulmonary thromboembolism?

139. Thrombo-prophylaxis during pregnancy. *5 (June 2017)*

140.a) Enumerate high risk factors for thromboembolism during pregnancy and puerperium. *4+6 (June 2016)*

b) How will you manage a G2P1L1 with history of DVT in the previous pregnancy?

141.a) What are the risk factors for venous thrombo-embolism?

b) How will you diagnose DVT during pregnancy?

c) Outline the plan of management of DVT n a primigravida with 30 weeks of pregnancy. *3+3+4 (Dec 2013)*

OLIGOHYDRAMNIOS

142.a) Define oligohydramnios.

b) What are the causes of oligohydramnios?

c) Discuss the management of ART conceived antenatal woman at 32 weeks pregnancy with oligohydramnios. *2+3+5 (April 2023)*

PREMATURITY

143.G2 with history of PTL. *2+4+4 (June 2025)*

a) Management at 25 weeks with CL 2.1 cm.

b) Rescue cerclage pros & cons.

c) Early neonatal complications of preterm.

144.a) Enumerate the causes of preterm labor and its risk factors in pregnant women. *4+6 (May 2024)*

b) Discuss the management of a pregnant woman with premature preterm rupture of membrane at 28 weeks period of gestation.

145.a) Discuss etiology and prediction of preterm labour.

b) A 30-year-old second gravida has reported to labour room at 30 weeks gestation with preterm labor. Discuss management. *5+5 (Oct 2023)*

146.a) What are the causes of early neonatal death in preterm neonates?

b) Discuss the management of 30-year-old G3P2Lo. presenting in ANC OPD at 25 weeks of gestation with the history of preterm early neonatal deaths in previous pregnancies. *2+8 (June 2021)*

147.a) What are the risk factors for prematurity? *2+4+4 (June 2018)*

b) Describe the complications of prematurity.

c) What are the interventions to minimize prematurity related complications?

148.a) What are the clinical criteria of preterm labour? *3+4+3 (June 2017)*

b) Prediction and prevention of preterm labour.

c) Role of Atosiban as a tocolytic agent.

149.a) What are the major short & long term problems with very low birth weight infants? *4+3+3 (April 2016)*

b) What is the pathophysiology of preterm labour?

c) What are the preventive strategies to prevent preterm delivery?

150.a) How will you identify women at risk for spontaneous preterm labour?

b) Discuss management of PPROM (Preterm premature rupture of membranes). *6+4 (Dec 2014)*

151.a) What are the etiological factors and clinical evidence of preterm labour? *4+3+3 (June 2013)*

b) What are the steps to prevent preterm labour?

c) Classify tocolytic agents used in preterm labour.

PROM & PPROM

152.a) Diagnosis of premature rupture of membranes. *4+6 (June 2020)*

b) Management protocol of a primigravida at 30 weeks attending with leakage of liquor.

153.a) What are the causes of PPROM? *3+3+4 (June 2016)*

b) How will you confirm the diagnosis of PPROM?

c) How will you manage a case of PPROM at 33 weeks of gestation?

154.a) Define PPROM. *2+2+6 (April 2016)*

b) What are the risk factors?

c) How will you manage a case of PPROM at 28 weeks of pregnancy?

155. A primigravida with 8 months of amenorrhoea has history of leaking per vaginum.

a) How will you confirm the diagnosis? *2+4+4 (June 2015)*

b) What investigations would you like to do in this case?

c) How would you mange her?

CERVICAL INCOMPETENCE

156. G2 with history of PTL.

a) Management at 25 weeks with CL 2.1 cm. *2+4 (June 2025)*

b) Rescue cerclage pros & cons.

157.a) Define cervical incompetence. *3+4+3 (April 2016)*

b) What are its causes?

c) How will you diagnose and manage a case of cervical incompetence at 14 weeks of pregnancy?

158.a) Causes of cervical insufficiency. *3+4+3 (Dec 2015)*

b) Postoperative management following cerclage operation.

c) Abdominal cerclage operation.

INFECTIONS IN PREGNANCY

159.a) Describe causes of fever in pregnancy and puerperium.

b) Discuss the management of malaria in pregnancy. *5+5 (Dec 2022)*

160.a) What is the symptomology of COVID-19 infection during pregnancy?

b) Discuss COVID-19 vaccination during pregnancy. *5+5 (June 2021)*

161.a) How will you optimize antenatal care during COVID-19 pandemic?

b) Management of suspected/ confirmed COVID-19 case during labour.

c) How will you manage a baby born to such mother? *4+4+2 (June 2020)*

162.a) Effect of Rubella infection on the foetus and its prevention.

b) Safety of vaccination during pregnancy. *6+4 (Dec 2016)*

163.a) What is Zika virus? *1+2+2+3+2 (June 2016)*

b) How is it transmitted?

c) How is the infection diagnosed in pregnant woman?

d) How is foetus affected?

e) Should amniocentesis be considered for diagnosis of congenital Zika virus infection?

164.a) Enumerate the viral infections that are associated with congenital malformation. *5+5 (April 2016)*

b) How will you manage a case of dengue fever during pregnancy?

165. Management of genital wart during pregnancy. *4 (April 2016)*

166.a) What is congenital rubella syndrome? *3+3+4 (Dec 2015)*

b) Diagnosis of rubella infections in pregnant women and fetus.

c) Outline the management of a pregnant woman who is exposed to rubella infection in her 11 weeks of gestation.

167. Discuss the management of pregnancy in a women who had chicken pox at 26 weeks of gestation. *10 (Dec 2014)*

168.a) Discuss malarial infestation in pregnancy. *3+4+3 (Dec 2012)*

b) What are the complications requiring closer monitoring during pregnancy?

c) Discuss treatment of malaria in pregnancy.

NON IMMUNE HYDROPS

169.a) Define NIH. *2+4+4 (June 2025)*
b) Common causes by gestation.
c) Counseling for fetal autopsy in IUFD with NIH.

170.a) Describe the etiologies of non-immune fetal hydrops. *4+6 (May 2024)*
b) Discuss the evaluation of a case of non-immune fetal hydrops antenatally and work up of a neonate diagnosed after birth.

171.a) What is non immune hydrops fetalis (NIHF)? *2+8 (June 2021)*
b) How will you manage a case of NIHF at 26 weeks of gestation and when will you like to deliver her?

172.a) Etio-pathogenesis of non-immune hydrops. *5+5 (June 2018)*
b) How will you manage a case of non-immune hydrops at 26 weeks of pregnancy?

PRE-CONCEPTIONAL CARE

173.a) Discuss pre-conceptional counseling and care in high risk mother.
b) Describe first trimester screenig methods and its importance. *5+5 (Oct 2023)*

174.a) What is preconception counselling? *2+8 (June 2021)*
b) How will you do pre conceptional counselling in 24 year old nulliparous woman with rheumatic heart disease with mitral stenosis?

175.a) Define pre-conceptional care. What are its clinical applications.
b) How will you investigate and manage a woman with history of congenital heart disease in previous baby? *5+5 (June 2018)*

176.a) What is pre-conceptional counselling? *2+4+4 (Dec 2011)*
b) Describe the role of pre-conceptional counselling in obstetrics.
c) How will you counsel a newly married woman with RHD and mitral stenosis?

ANTENATAL CARE

177.a) Describe various methods of antepartum foetal screening. *3 (Dec 2022)*
b) Discuss non-invasive techniques for prenatal diagnosis for foetal anomalies. *3+7 (Dec 2022)*

178.a) How will you date a pregnancy? *5+5 (June 2018)*
b) How do you manage a pregnant women past expected date of delivery?

179.a) What do you understand by antenatal care? *2+4+4 (June 2015)*

b) Investigative facilities for antenatal care that should be available in a tertiary care centre.

c) How will you counsel a low risk pregnant women in early antenatal period?

180.a) Enumerate the key points in setting up an ideal antenatal clinic in your environment. *5+5 (Dec 2012)*

b) How do you propose to maintain a system to minimize drop-out rate?

HYPEREMESIS

181.a) Define hyperemesis gravidarum. *2+ (2+2) +4 (Dec 2015)*

b) Its clinical features and complications.

c) Management of hyperemesis gravidarum.

182.a) Define hyperemesis gravidarum. *3+4+3 (June 2013)*

b) What are its clinical features and complications?

c) Discuss its differential diagnosis.

RPL

183.a) Enlist various etiologies for recurrent pregnancy loss and describe work up of a case of recurrent pregnancy loss. *4+6 (May 2024)*

b) Discuss the antenatal and postnatal management of a pregnant woman with previous 2 missed abortions diagnosed as APLA syndrome at 20 weeks period of gestation.

184.a) What are the causes of recurrent pregnancy loss? *3+7 (April 2023)*

b) Describe the management of a woman with history of recurrent pregnancy loss.

185.a) Causes of recurrent pregnancy loss (RPL). *2+2+6 (June 2019)*

b) Significance of pedigree chart.

c) Genetic counselling in recurrent pregnancy loss.

186.a) What are the causes of recurrent pregnancy loss? *5+5 (Dec 2019)*

b) Role of low molecular weight heparin in its treatment.

187.a) What are the causes of recurrent pregnancy loss? *2+4+4 (Dec 2016)*

b) How will you evaluate a non-pregnant woman having of three abortions?

c) Outline the plan of management of a pregnant woman having history of three intrauterine deaths at term.

188.a) Define recurrent pregnancy loss. *2+4+4 (April 2016)*
b) What are the causes of RPL?
c) How will you investigate such a case?

189.a) What are the causes of recurrent foetal loss? *3+3+4 (June 2013)*
b) Define and classify thrombophilia in pregnancy.
c) Describe the clinical approach to the management of early pregnancy with APLA.

SLE/APLA/BOH

190.a) What is the effect of SLE on pregnancy? *2+8 (June 2019)*
b) Diagnosis & management of a case of pregnancy with APLA syndrome.

191. SLE in pregnancy. *5 (June 2016)*

192.a) Enumerate the causes of second trimester abortions.
b) How will you investigate a case of recurrent second trimester abortions and prognosticate the woman about chances of such abortions in her subsequent pregnancy? *3+ (4+3) (June 2015)*

193.a) What are anti-phospholipid antibodies? *2+5+3 (Dec 2015)*
b) Clinical and laboratory criteria of diagnosing anti-phospholipid antibody syndrome.
c) Pregnancy complications associated with thrombophilia.

194.a) What do you understand by BOH (Bad obstetric history)?
b) How will you investigate in interval phase and during pregnancy? *3+ (4+3) (Dec 2014)*

195.a) What are the maternal and perinatal effects of pregnancy with SLE?
b) How would you monitor a woman with SLE during pregnancy, child birth and postpartum? *(2+2)+ (2+2+2) (June 2014)*

IUD/STILL BIRTH

196.a) Discuss the causes of still birth. *5+5 (April 2023)*
b) What measures will you take to prevent perinatal death?

197. An unbooked primigravida patient at 32 weeks pregnancy reports to OPD with intrauterine device. *2+2+6 (June 2018)*
a) What are the causes of IUD in this patient?
b) What are the complications of IUD?
c) How will you manage this patent?

198.a) Enumerate the causes of still birth. *3+5+2 (April 2016)*

b) Mention various ways by which how you will evaluate a still born infant.
c) How will you counsel the parents?

199.a) What are the causes of still births? *4+6 (June 2014)*
b) How will you evaluate a patient with a previous history of still births?

PUERPERIUM

200.a) What is exclusive breast feeding? *3+3+4 (April 2023)*
b) Advantages of breast feeding.
c) Discuss the role of drugs used to suppress lactation.

201. A 28 year old para 2 woman presents 24 hours after vaginal delivery with severe sepsis. Delivery was at home in a village conducted by a Dai:
a) Define maternal sepis. *2+3+5 (June 2022)*
b) What are the risk factors for maternal sepsis?
c) How will you diagnose and manage a case of maternal sepsis?

202.a) Define puerperal pyrexia. Enumerate the causes of puerperal pyrexia.
b) How will you manage a case of puerperal sepsis in a primiparous woman? *5+5 (Dec 2020)*

203.a) What is puerperal sepsis? *2+3+5 (June 2019)*
b) Predisposing factors for puerperal sepsis.
c) Management of puerperal sepsis.

204.a) What is postpartum blues? *2+4+4 (June 2019)*
b) Risk factors and impact of postpartum depression.
c) Treatment approaches for postpartum depression.

205.a) What are the predisposing factors of puerperal sepsis?
b) How will you investigate and manage a case of puerperal sepsis?
c) Describe in brief its long term impact on reproductive health.
3+4+3 (June 2013)

H MOLE

206.a) Describe classification of GTD and pathogenesis of gestational trophoblastic diseases. *4+6 (Dec 2022)*
b) Discuss management of patient with H.mole with coexisting live fetus at 14 weeks of gestation.

DIC

207.a) Pathogenesis of DIC. *5+5 (Dec 2018)*
b) How will you manage DIC?

SCAR PREGNANCY

208.a) Types of ectopic pregnancy. *2+4+4 (June 2025)*
b) Workup of caesarean scar pregnancy.
c) Management of scar pregnancy.

OTHERS

209.a) Descibe the tests done for antepartum fetal surveillance in the first trimester in pregnancy. *6+4 (April 2023)*
b) Respectful maternity case.

210. Immunisation during pregnancy. *5 (April 2023)*

211.a) Discuss etiopathology and diagnosis of incompetent cervix and types of cerclage. *6+4 (Dec 2022)*
b) Describe management of cervical incompetency at 18 weeks in a patient with history of RPL.

212.a) Write a note on role of umbilical coiling Index and its significance.
b) Discuss types of cord insertion.
c) Discuss diagnosis and management of vasa previa. *3+2+5 (Dec 2022)*

213.a) How to diagnose caesarean scar pregnancy? *2+2+6 (June 2022)*
b) Enlist various risk factors for caesarean scar pregnancy.
c) Describe the various management options for caesarean scar pregnancy.

214.a) What are the causes of decreased foetal movements in the third trimester of pregnancy? *2+8 (June 2021)*
b) Discuss the management of a primigravida at 36 weeks of gestation with decreased foetal movements.

215.a) Methods for the assessment of gestational age. *2+2+6 (June 2019)*
b) What are the indices of foetal maturity?

216. Pregnancy of unknown location (PUL). *5 (Dec 2016)*

217.a) Critically evaluate the role of laparoscopic myomectomy.
b) What factors contribute to a weak scar?
c) How will you manage pregnancy in a woman after laparoscopic myomectomy? *3+3+4 (Dec 2016)*

218. Write brief notes on: *3+3+4 (June 2013)*
a) Exclusive breast feeding.
b) Post-partum thyroid disease.
c) Prevention of Rh isoimmunisation.

CHAPTER

10

LABOUR

SHOULDER DYSTOCIA

1. a) Enumerate causes of shoulder dystocia. *4+6 (May 2024)*
   b) Describe the management of a case of shoulder dystocia.

2. Discuss the management of woman with shoulder dystocia. *4 (April 2023)*

3. Shoulder dystocia. *5 (Dec 2020)*

4. a) How will you diagnose shoulder dystocia in labour? *2+2+6 (June 2019)*
   b) Complications of shoulder dystocia.
   c) Management of shoulder dystocia in labour.

5. a) What are the risk factors for prediction of shoulder dystocia?
   b) What are the possible maternal and foetal complications of shoulder dystocia?
   c) Discuss the management of shoulder dystocia. *2+3+5 (Dec 2013)*

6. a) What are the predisposing factors for shoulder dystocia?
   b) Discuss salient guidelines for managing such a case.
   c) What are the maternal and neonatal complications of shoulder dystocia? *3+4+3 (Dec 2012)*

VBAC/TOLAC

7. a) Favorable factors for TOLAC. *2 (June 2025)*
   b) Signs/symptoms of scar rupture.

8. a) Define trail of labour. *2+2+2+4 (June 2019)*
   b) What are the indications for trail labour?
   c) What are the favourable and unfavourable factors in trail labour?
   d) How will you conduct trail labour?

9. a) What is VBAC? *4+6 (Dec 2014)*
   b) Discuss factors favourable for VBAC.

10. a) What are the pre-requisites of Vaginal Birth After Caesarean (VBAC)?
    b) How will you counsel a patient to participate for VBAC?

c) How would you monitor a patient of previous caesarean section during labour? *3+3+4 (Dec 2013)*

LSCS

11.a) How to do cesarean section audit and role of obstetricians to reduce caesarean epidemic? *4+6 (May 2024)*

b) Enumerate life threatening conditions in pregnancy due to previous caesarean sections in each trimester. Describe diagnosis and management of each enlisted condition.

12.a) Robson's criteria for cesarean section. *5+5 (April 2023)*

b) Indications of TOLAC and monitoring of a case of previous LSCS in labour.

13. Strategies to reduce caesarean section rates. *5 (June 2021)*

14.a) Robson classification for LSCS. *4+3+3 (Dec 2018)*

b) List the common causes contributing to rising rates of Caesarean section.

c) Counselling of pregnant woman seeking caesarean on demand.

15.a) Pros and cons of elective caesarean section on demand.

b) Neonatal morbidity in elective caesarean section.

c) Previous caesarean scar pregnancy. *3+4+3 (June 2017)*

INDUCTION OF LABOUR (IOL)

16.a) Describe the Bishop's score. *4+6 (May 2024)*

b) Describe various drugs used for induction of labor- indications, contraindications, dosage and side effects.

17.a) Cervical ripening agents. *4+3+3 (April 2023)*

b) Discuss the various uterotonic drugs.

c) Various methods of cervical ripening.

18. Induction of labour. *5 (Dec 2020)*

19.a) What is the difference between augmentation and induction of labour?

b) List the prerequisites of IOL.

c) Describe the various methods of IOL. *2+2+6 (June 2018)*

20.a) Advantages of active management of labour (AMOL). *3+3+4 (Dec 2015)*

b) Different methods for induction and augmentation of labour.

c) Factors which predict successful induction of labour.

PERINEAL TEARS

22.a) Classify perineal tear. *4+4+2 (June 2025)*

b) Stepwise management of complete tear with diagram.

c) Post-op care.

23. Describe the steps of repair of 3c perineal tear. *4 (June 2025)*

24.a) With help of diagrams, describe anatomy of perineum. *5+5 (Oct 2023)*

b) Discuss management of a 30 year old primipara who reported to your OPD on Day four postpartum with a difficult home delivery and is found to have a complete perineal tear.

25.a) Discuss the management of Obstetrics anal sphincter injury syndrome (OASIS). *5+5 (April 2023)*

b) Discuss one hour sepsis bundle.

26.a) What are the causes of cervical tear during delivery? *3+4+3 (June 2018)*

b) How will you suspect and diagnose a case of cervical tear?

c) How will you manage such a case?

BIRTH INJURIES

27.a) Classify birth injuries. *4+6 (Dec 2012)*

b) How do you anticipate and prevent them?

INTRA-PARTUM

28.a) Components of WHO labour care guide. *5+5 (June 2025)*

b) Advantages/disadvantages over partogram.

29.a) FIGO consensus on CTG. *5+5 (June 2025)*

b) Interpretation of computerized cCTG.

30.a) Describe the physiology of labour. *4 (April 2023)*

31.a) Describe abnormal labor. *3+3 (April 2023)*

b) Current WHO partograph.

32.a) Discuss diagnosis and management of a primigravida patient with 41 plus 2 days weeks of gestational age not in labour. *8+2 (Dec 2022)*

b) Discuss the interpretation of abnormal CTG finding.

33.a) Define Partogram. *2+8 (June 2021)*

b) Discuss the New labour care guidelines of WHO 2020.

34.a) What are the various modalities of intra-partum foetal surveillance in high risk pregnancy? *5+5 (June 2018)*

b) Role of intrauterine resuscitation in cases of intra-partum foetal distress.

35. Intra-partum foetal monitoring. *5 (Dec 2016)*

36.a) Indications for electronic foetal monitoring (EFM). *3+4+3 (April 2016)*

b) Causes of intrapartum foetal bradycardia and tachycardia.

c) How will you manage late deceleration?

37. Admission test at onset of labour. *3 (June 2013)*

38.a) Describe the methods of intrapartum foetal monitoring. *4+3 (June 2012)*

b) What do you understand by normal tracing and abnormal tracing observed during electronic fetal monitoring?

LABOR MANAGEMENT

39.a) What is active management of third stage of labour? *5+5 (Dec 2019)*

b) Describe the surgical management of atonic post-partum haemorrhage.

40. What is the active management of third stage of labour? *4 (April 2016)*

41.a) Anatomy of lower uterine segment in pregnancy and its role in labour.

b) What are the clinical features of obstructed labour in CPD?

c) Difficulties in 2nd stage LSCS. *4+3+3 (June 2017)*

42.a) Delivery of second twin. *5+5 (June 2015)*

b) Embryo reduction.

43.a) Define active phase of labour. *2+ (4+4) (June 2014)*

b) Enumerate its abnormalities and their management.

LABOR ANALGESIA

44.a) Briefly discuss various modalities of labour analgesia. *5+5 (Oct 2023)*

b) Discuss in detail indications, contraindications, pros and cons of epidural analgesia in labour.

45.a) Describe role of epidural analgesia in labour. *4+4+2 (June 2022)*

b) Discuss the pros and cons of water birth.

c) Describe the role of morphine in labour - advantages and disadvantages.

46.a) Enumerate the methods of labour analgesia. *3+2+ (2+3) (Dec 2015)*

b) Contraindications for neuraxial analgesia.

c) Post-dural puncture headache and its management.

MAL-PRESENTATIONS

47. Four possible outcomes of ROP position & management. *5 (June 2025)*

48.a) Define external cephalic version. *2+8 (Aug 2021)*

b) What are the prerequisites and complications of external cephalic version.

49.a) Enumerate causes of breech presentation in pregnant women.

b) Discuss the management options for multigravida with breech presentation at term gestation. *4+6 (June 2022)*

50.a) Methods of delivery of after-coming head in breech presentations.

b) Management of neglected shoulder presentation. *5+5 (Dec 2020)*

51.a) Management of after coming head of breech. *5+5 (Dec 2019)*

b) Precautions to be taken in delivery of premature breech.

52.a) Discuss occipito-posterior position, its management during labour with special emphasis on face o pubis delivery. *3+4+3 (Dec 2014)*

53. A multigravida with 9 month of amenorrhoea has a transverse lie.

a) What investigations would you like to do and why? *(2+3)+5 (June 2015)*

b) How would you manage her?

54.a) What are the predisposing factors for breech presentation?

b) How will you manage such a case presenting at 36 weeks? *3+7 (June 2014)*

55.a) What are the causes of foetal mal-presentations in term pregnancy?

b) Enumerate the obstetric complications of foetal mal-presentations.

c) Describe the current guidelines and protocol of external cephalic version. *3+3+4 (June 2013)*

56. a) What are the indications of induction of labour? *3+3+4 (Dec 2012)*

b) Enumerate the Bishop's score and mention its significance.

c) What are the methods of induction and highlight the method and uses of oxytocin?

INSTRUMENTAL DELIVERY

57.a) Discuss the prerequisites and indications of vacuum assisted delivery.

b) Compare the advantages, disadvantages and complications of vacuum assisted delivery with forceps delivery. *4+6 (May 2024)*

CHAPTER

11

OBSTETRIC EMERGENCIES

MATERNAL COLLAPSE

1. a) List the differential diagnosis of a case of postpartum breathlessness presenting 24 hours post-delivery. *2 (May 2024)*

2. a) Describe causes of maternal collapse in pregnancy. *4+6 (Dec 2022)*
   b) Discuss the approach to maternal collapse.

3. a) Define maternal near miss and its various aetiologies. *6+4 (June 2022)*
   b) Discuss the work up plan for sudden maternal collapse in labour.

4. a) Resuscitation in a critically ill patient with advanced pregnancy.
   b) Sudden postpartum collapse and its management. *5+5 (June 2017)*

5. a) What is postpartum collapse? *2+3+5 (June 2015)*
   b) Enumerate its causes.
   c) How will you manage a case of amniotic fluid embolism in a primiparous woman just after delivery?

AMNIOTIC FLUID EMBOLISM

6. A young multigravida presents to casualty at term pregnancy with acute onset of severe breathlessness.
   a) Discuss the differential diagnosis. *5+5 (Dec 2018)*
   b) Describe the workup of the woman to reach the diagnosis.

7. a) Etiopathogenesis of amniotic fluid embolism. *3+3 (April 2016)*
   b) Management and prognosis of amniotic fluid management.

8. a) What is postpartum collapse? *2+3+5 (June 2015)*
   b) Enumerate its causes.
   c) How will you manage a case of amniotic fluid embolism in a primiparous woman just after delivery?

9. a) What is postpartum collapse? *2+3+5 (Dec 2013)*
   b) Enumerate its causes.
   c) How will you manage a case of amniotic fluid embolism in a primiparous woman just after delivery?

10.a) Physiological mechanism of formation of amniotic fluid embolism.

b) Enumerate the etiological factors of oligohydramnios.

c) How will you manage a primigravida with 34 weeks pregnancy and AFI 5 cm? *3+2+5 (June 2013)*

DIC

11.a) Describe the changes in coagulation factors in pregnancy.

b) Management of DIC in pregnancy. *5+5 (Oct 2023)*

RUPTURE UTERUS

12. Gravida 2 para 1 at 38 period of gestation with previous caesarean scar has presented with loss of foetal movements: *5+5 (June 2022)*

a) List the possible differential diagnosis for the above case.

b) Discuss the various management options for above differentials.

13.a) Define rupture of the uterus. *2+8 (June 2019)*

b) Diagnosis and management of uterine rupture.

14.a) What do you understand by Bandl's ring? *4+ (3+3) (Dec 2014)*

b) Describe the clinical picture and management of rupture uterus.

RETAINED PLACENTA

15.a) Enumerate causes of retained placenta. *4+6 (June 2022)*

b) Describe the various management options for a case of retained placenta.

UTERINE INVERSION

16.a) How will you classify uterine inversion? *2+8 (June 2021)*

b) Discuss the management of uterine inversion following vaginal delivery.

17.a) Acute inversion of uterus. *5+5 (Dec 2020)*

b) Management of postpartum haemorrhage.

18. a. Define acute uterine inversion. *2+ (2+2+4) (June 2016)*

b) Risk factors, diagnosis and outline the plan of management for acute uterine inversion.

PERI-PARTUM HYSTERECTOMY

19.a) Indications of peri-partum hysterectomy. *2+4+4 (June 2016)*

b) What are the complications associated with peri-partum hysterectomy?

c) Outline its post-operative management.

20.a) Write indications for peripartum hysterectomy. *4+6 (June 2014)*

b) What are the consequences of massive blood loss in obstetrics?

ANTE-PARTUM HAEMORRHAGE

21. Gravida 2 para 1 at 38 period of gestation presents with loss of fetal movements and sudden pain abdomen. On examination, her BP is 140/90mm Hg. Her abdomen is tense and tender. Foetal heart is not localised and dark colored bleeding per vaginum is present:

a) Discuss the differential diagnoses for the above case.

b) Discuss the management of this case. *4+6 (May 2024)*

POSTPARTUM HAEMORRHAGE

22.a) Define secondary PPH & causes. *4+4 (June 2025)*

b) Massive blood transfusion protocol.

23.a) What changes occur in uterine muscles in pregnancy?

b) Enumerate the steps of active management of third stage of labour.

c) Discuss the management of atonic PPH. *2+3+5 (Oct 2024)*

24. Describe the stepwise management of atonic postpartum hemorrhage. *6 (May 2024)*

25.a) Define massive blood loss. *2+2+2+4 (June 2019)*

b) How will you estimate blood loss?

c) Significance of golden hour management.

d) Steps for resuscitation.

26.a) Causes of postpartum haemorrhage. *3+4+3 (Dec 2015)*

b) Outline the management of a case which is unresponsive to uterotonic agents.

c) Enumerate complications of blood transfusion.

27.a) Bilateral ligation of internal iliac arteries in obstetrics. *3+3+4 (Dec 2015)*

b) Selection of a patient for admission in an intensive care unit.

28.a) What are the causes of massive obstetric haemorrhage?

b) Outline emergency obstetric management in atonic post-partum haemorrhage.

c) What are its immediate and late complications? *3+4+3 (June 2013)*

29. What are the complications of massive transfusion? *3 (Dec 2012)*

DTA

30.a) Define deep transverse arrest (DTA) and its various aetiologies.
b) Discuss the management options of DTA.
c) Describe the complications in neonate born after DTA. *4+4+2 (June 2022)*

OBSTRUCTED LABOUR

31.a) Enumerate the complications which can happen while doing Caesarean section for obstructed labour.
b) What preventive measures should be taken to avoid intraoperative and postoperative complications while doing Caesarean section for obstructed labour?
c) Discuss the managment of these complications. *2+3+5 (April 2023)*

32.a) Define obstructed labour. *1+3+3+3 (Dec 2013)*
b) Enlist its causes.
c) How do you diagnose it?
d) Enumerate its maternal and foetal complications of obstructed labour.

SHOCK IN OBSTETRICS

33.a) Define shock in obstetrics. *2+4+4 (Dec 2013)*
b) Enumerate the causes and phases of endotoxic shock.
c) How will you manage a case of septic shock in pregnancy?

34.a) Enumerate the causes and describe the management of septic shock in obstetrics. *6+4 (June 2012)*
b) What are its anti-shock trousers or devices?
c) Describe their use in obstetrics and gynaecology.

PERIPARTUM CARDIOMYOPATHY

35.b) Describe the management of a postnatal case diagnosed with peripartum cardiomyopathy. *6 (May 2024)*

36.a) What is peripartum cardiomyopathy? *3+4+3 (June 2013)*
b) What are its clinical features and prognosis?
c) Describe the management of congestive cardiac failure in association with peripartum cardiomyopathy in term pregnancy.

CHAPTER

12

NEONATOLOGY

NEONATAL JAUNDICE

1. a) Discuss neonatal jaundice. *5 (April 2023)*

2. a) Discuss causes of jaundice in newborn. *(4+3+3) Dec 2018*
   b) What is the rationale for phototherapy in neonatal hyperbilirubinemia?
   c) What is basic care of newborn during phototherapy?

3. a) Causes, clinical features and complications of pathological jaundice in a newborn. *(2+2+2)+4 (June 2016)*
   b) How does exchange transfusion help a neonate with Rh iso-immunization?

4. a) What are the causes of neonatal jaundice? *4+ (3+3) (Dec 2014)*
   b) Discuss in brief kernicterus and role of phototherapy in its management.

NEONATAL SEPSIS

5. Early onset neonatal sepsis - diagnosis and prevention. *5 (June 2021)*

6. a) Define and classify neonatal sepsis. *5+5 (Dec 2020)*
   b) Outline the management of neonatal sepsis.

RDS

7. a) What is respiratory distress syndrome? *3+2+5 (Dec 2019)*
   b) Differential diagnosis of respiratory distress in the neonate.
   c) Management of respiratory distress syndrome.

BIRTH ASPHYXIA

8. a) Define birth asphyxia. *3+4+3 (April 2016)*
   b) What is modified biophysical profile score?
   c) What is the role of admission test?

9. a) What is birth asphyxia? *3+4+3 (June 2013)*
   b) What are the preventive steps to avoid birth asphyxia in growth restricted babies?

c) Enumerate the long term effects of birth asphyxia.

KANGAROO MOTHER CARE

10. Kangaroo mother care. *5 (Oct 2023)*

11. a) Describe 'Baby friendly hospital initiatives'. *5+5 (Dec 2022)*
    b) Discuss 'Kangaroo Mother Care'.

12. Kangaroo mother care. *5 (Dec 2020)*

13. Neonatal resuscitation. *5 (Dec 2020)*

14. What is kangaroo care? *4 (June 2014)*

CORTICOSTEROID THERAPY

15. a) Critically appraise the role of antenatal corticosteroid therapy.
    b) Describe the various drugs, dosage and recommendations of antenatal corticosteroid therapy. *5+5 (May 2024)*

16. Discuss pros, cons and various regimes and mechanism of action of antenatal steroids administered to mother for fetal lung maturation. *5 (Oct 2023)*

17. a) Role of antenatal corticosteroid therapy - advantages and disadvantages.
    b) Describe the various drug, dosage and recommendations of antenatal corticosteroid therapy. *5+5 (June 2022)*

18. Antenatal corticosteroids. *5 (Dec 2020)*

NEONATAL RESUSCITATION

19. Outline the management of a neonate with birth asphyxia at birth. *5 (April 2023)*

20. Give outline of neonatal resuscitation of a live baby delivered vaginally at term and who has no spontaneous breathing efforts. *5+5 (Oct 2023)*

21. Neonatal resuscitation. *5 (Dec 2020)*

22. Apgar score. *5 (Dec 2020)*

23. a) Cardiopulmonary adjustments in a newborn child. *4+2+4 (June 2016)*
    b) Draw an algorithm for steps of neonatal resuscitation.
    c) List eight maternal conditions warranting the presence of neonatal resuscitation team at the time of delivery.

24.a) Physiology of initiation of air breathing of foetus after delivery.
b) How would you evaluate the condition of newborn?
c) Enumerate the basic resuscitation protocols for a newborn in the delivery room. *3+3+4 (Dec 2015)*

25.a) How is the condition of a newborn evaluated at birth? *5+5 (June 2015)*
b) What is the algorithm of resuscitation protocol in a newborn?

26.a) Describe the essential steps of neonatal resuscitation. *6+4 (June 2014)*
b) What is kangaroo care?

27.a) What is APGAR score? *2+4+4 (Dec 2011)*
b) Describe the resuscitation of a newborn baby with poor APGAR score.
c) Define birth asphyxia and enumerate its immediate and long term sequalae.

CEPHALOHEMATOMA

28.a) How to differentiate caput succedaneum, subgaleal haematoma and cephalhematoma? *5+5 (June 2020)*
b) Causes and management of each of them.

29.a) What is cephalo-haematoma? *3+ (3+4) (Dec 2014)*
b) Describe its aetiology and management?

OTHERS

30.a) Describe the aetiologies of non-immune fetal hydrops. *4+6 (May 2024)*
b) Discuss the evaluation of a case of non-immune fetal hydrops antenatally and work up of a neonate diagnosed after birth.

31. Convulsions in newborn. *5 (Oct 2023)*

32. Describe management of Rh isoimmunised neonate. *2 (June 2022)*

33. Discuss the management of a neonate born to HIV positive woman. *5 (June 2021)*

34.a) Essential newborn care. *4+3+3 (June 2020)*
b) Neonatal jaundice.
c) Hypoxic ischemic encephalopathy.

35.a) Enumerate congenital malformations in new-born which are surgical emergencies. *2+2+6 (June 2019)*
b) Diagnosis and management of trachea-oesophageal fistula.

36. How will you care for a newborn of: *2x5 (June 2016)*
    a) Diabetic mother
    b) Rh –ve mother
    c) HIV +ve mother
    d) Epileptic mother
    e) Beta thalassemia trait +ve mother

37. What are the neonatal complications of infant of diabetic mother? *3 (April 2016)*

38.a) Immediate care and follow up of a baby born to Rh –ve mother. *3+2+ (1+2+2) (June 2015)*
    b) RDS in newborn – Definition, causes and prophylactic measures.

39.a) What are the complications can occur in a new-born of a diabetic mother? *3+3+4 (Dec 2013)*
    b) How can this be prevented?
    c) Discuss the management of neonatal hypoglycaemia.

40.a) What are the benefits of breast feeding to the mother and newborn? *4+3 (Dec 2013)*
    b) Discuss galactogenesis and lactogenesis.

41. Write briefly on: *3+3 (June 2013)*
    a) Hypoxic ischaemic encephalopathy.
    b) Neonatal jaundice.

42.a) What are the causes of foetal anaemia? *2+4+4 (Dec 2012)*
    b) Write the methods used to diagnose foetal anaemia?
    c) Management plan to treat it?

CHAPTER

13

HIV

1. a) Discuss the antepartum management of primigravida presenting at 24 weeks of gestation with HIV status positive. *5+3+2 (May 2024)*
   b) Discuss the management of labour in an HIV positive pregnant woman.
   c) Management of neonate born to HIV positive mother.
2. NACO new technical Guidelines for prevention of mother to child transmission of HIV. *5 (April 2023)*
3. Discuss the 4 essential components of prevention of HIV infection in pregnant woman and the neonate. *10 (Dec 2022)*
4. Mrs. Y 33 years G3P2L2 at 12 weeks comes to OPD with HIV test reported as positive.
   a) Discuss the management of this case in antenatal period.
   b) Discuss the recommendations for breast feeding and infant prophylaxis at birth. *5+5 (Dec 2021)*
5. Discuss the management of a neonate born to HIV positive woman. *5 (June 2021)*
6. a) Effect of HIV infection on pregnancy. *2+2+6 (Dec 2019)*
   b) Effect of pregnancy on HIV infection.
   c) Measures to prevent parent to child transmission of HIV.
7. a) Current national guidelines for antenatal management for preventive of vertical transmission of HIV from mother to newborn. *5+5 (Dec 2018)*
   b) Current national guidelines for follow up care of neonate born to a HIV seropositive mother.
8. a) What is vertical transmission? *2+4+4 (June 2018)*
   b) What are the risk factors for the transmission of HIV?
   c) How will you prevent vertical transmission of HIV infection from mother to baby?
9. a) Factors influencing perinatal transmission of HIV infection.
   b) What are its preventive measures?
   c) Current WHO recommendations on neonatal management of HIV infected mothers. *4+3+3 (June 2017)*

10. a) Current recommendations for management of HIV positive pregnant women. *5+ (2+3) (April 2016)*
    b) Give details of intra-partum and postpartum management.

11. a) What are the current recommendations for management of HIV positive pregnant women? *4+6 (June 2014)*
    b) What are the recommendations for management of delivery in such women and their neonates?

12. Discuss the recent guidelines for breast feeding for HIV positive women in developing countries. *3 (Dec 2013)*

13. Describe briefly post exposure prophylaxis against HIV. *3 (June 2013)*

14. a) What is the natural history of human HIV infection? *3+3+4 (June 2013)*
    b) What are the tests for HIV infections in pregnant women?
    c) How will you prevent perinatal transmission of HIV infection in pregnant women?

CHAPTER

14

SPM

NATIONAL PROGRAMS

1. Enumerate the six interventions of Anemia Mukt Bharat program. *6 (Oct 2024)*

2. a) Describe components of SUMAN programme (Surakshit Matritva Aashwashan) and role of obstetricians in promoting it. *4+6 (May 2024)*
   b) Discuss the management and complications of a pregnancy in an elderly obese woman.

3. Describe “Anemia Mukt Bharat” initiative by Government of India. *2 (May 2024)*

4. Pradhan Mantri Surakshit Matritva Abhiyan. *5 (April 2023)*

5. Discuss various government schemes for improvement and prevention of anemia in pregnant and newborn in our country. *10 (Dec 2022)*

6. a) Describe the role of gynaecologist in promoting Rastriya Kishore Swasthya Karyakaram (RKSK). *4+6 (June 2022)*
   b) Discuss the management and complications of a pregnancy in adolescent girl.

7. a) Discuss the goals of National Rural Health Mission. *3+4 (Dec 2021)*
   b) Write a note on Lakshya.

8. a) Anaemia Mukt Bharat programme. *5+5 (Dec 2018)*
   b) National nutrition mission.

9. Enumerate benefits provided in JSSK scheme (Janani Shishu Suraksha Karyakram). *10 (Dec 2014)*

10. a) What is Janani Shishu Suraksha Karyakram (JSSK)? *2+3+5 (Dec 2013)*
    b) What are its components?
    c) What are the strategies for its successful outcome?

11. a) What are the maternal and child health programme of government of India? *3+4+3 (June 2013)*
    b) Describe the RCH-II and its achievement.
    c) What is the role of ASHA in the reproductive health care of rural women?

MATERNAL MORTALITY

12.a) Maternal mortality & three most common causes in India.
b) Preventive measures to reduce maternal mortality.
c) Schemes in ongoing national health programs. *3+3+4 (June 2025)*

13.a) Give WHO definition of maternal death. *2+2+6 (Oct 2024)*
b) Define maternal mortality ratio.
c) What is direct obstetric death and indirect obstetric death? Give 2 examples of each.

14.a) Define maternal mortality ratio (MMR). What is the current rate in India? What is the target of MMR to be achieved by 2030 under Sustainable Development Goals?
b) Discuss the reasons for variations of MMR in different states of India.
c) Describe various strategies to reduce MMR in India. *3+3+4 (May 2024)*

15. Discuss the strategies to prevent maternal mortality ratio. *5 (April 2023)*

16. Indicators of maternal, neonatal and child health. *5 (June 2021)*

17.a) Maternal near miss and severe acute maternal morbidity.
b) Criteria for identifying maternal near-miss cases. *5+5 (Dec 2018)*

18.a) Define maternal mortality. *1+3+6 (June 2016)*
b) List causes of maternal mortality in India.
c) Role of maternal death review in reducing maternal mortality.

19.a) Define maternal mortality. How is it calculated? *3+4+3 (April 2016)*
b) Enumerate the causes of maternal mortality.
c) What are the strategies to reduce maternal mortality?

20.a) Maternal near miss. *5+5 (Dec 2016)*
b) Obstetric audit.

21.a) Define perinatal mortality. How is it calculated? *2+3+5 (Dec 2015)*
b) Enumerate causes of perinatal deaths.
c) Outline the recommended evaluation procedures for a woman with still birth.

22.a) What is maternal mortality rate currently in India? *2+ (3+5) (June 2015)*
b) Factors responsible for high maternal mortality in India and measures to reduce maternal mortality.

23.a) Define Maternal Near Miss. What are the criteria given by WHO for labelling a patient as Maternal Near Miss? *2+5+3 (Dec 2013)*

b) Discuss the steps to reduce maternal morbidity and mortality.

24.a) Define Maternal Near Miss. What are the criteria given by WHO for labelling a patient as Maternal Near Miss? *2+5+3 (Dec 2013)*

b) Discuss the steps to reduce maternal morbidity and mortality.

STUDY DESIGNS

25.a) Describe randomized case control study design. *4+6 (May 2024)*

b) Describe various levels of evidence based on types of studies in research methodology.

26.a) Describe case control study. *4+6 (June 2022)*

b) Describe various levels of evidences based on types of studies in research methodology.

27.a) What are the types of analytic studies? *2+3+5 (Dec 2020)*

b) Principles of randomized controlled study.

c) CONSORT checklist.

28.a) What are the different types of research? *5+5 (June 2020)*

b) How do you frame a research question?

29.a) What are the various types of research studies that can be conducted?

b) Describe a plan of study to determine the role of exercise in the management of cases of gestational diabetes mellitus. *5+5 (June 2020)*

30.a) What is randomization? *2+4+4 (June 2020)*

b) Explain various types of random sampling techniques with examples.

c) Enumerate and define the various fertility indicators.

31.a) How will you form a hypothesis for your research? *2+2+3+3 (Dec 2019)*

b) Enumerate factors to make a strong scientific research.

c) Classify different types of research articles.

d) What is the importance of review of literature?

32.a) Define applied research. *5+5 (Dec 2019)*

b) What are the various methods of sampling?

33.a) Explain the difference between a longitudinal and cross sectional study using suitable examples. *3+4+3 (Dec 2016)*

b) How do you calculate sample size of a therapeutic trial?

c) How do you evaluate the scientific validity of a research study?

34.a) Enumerate WHO criteria for a screening programme?
b) Which gynaecological cancer fulfils most of these criteria?
c) Define sensitivity, specificity, positive predictive value, negative predictive value and confidence interval. *4+1+ (1x5) (June 2016)*

35.a) What is RCH? *4+3+3 (June 2015)*
b) What are its components?
c) What are the strategies for its successful outcome?

36. What do you understand by double blind placebo controlled trial and its significance? *7+3 (Dec 2014)*

37. Enumerate various types of scientific studies and their role in establishing levels of evidence and recommendations for clinical practice. *10 (June 2014)*

38.a) What are the aims, vision, goals and component of RCH?
b) State the differences between RCH I & II. *(2+2+2+2)+2 (Dec 2013)*

BIOMEDICAL WASTE MANAGEMENT

39.a) Biomedical waste management. *5+5 (May 2024)*
b) Describe standard precautions.

40.a) Biological waste disposal in labour room. *4+3+3 (June 2017)*
b) Universal precautions.
c) Post exposure prophylaxis.

ETHICS

41.a) Describe briefly the components of publication ethics.
b) Enumerate the types of plagiarism.
c) Discuss methods to avoid plagiarism. *4+3+3 (Dec 2022)*

42.a) Areas of medical litigations in obstetrics. *3+7 (Dec 2015)*
b) Measures to reduce medico legal problems in obstetrics (including legal and ethical issues).

43.a) What are the differences between implied consent and informed consent? *3+4+3 (Dec 2013)*
b) What are the potential areas of litigation in obstetrics?
c) Discuss the medico-legal aspects of birth asphyxia.

OTHERS

44.a) ASHA worker. *5+5 (Dec 2019)*

b) Describe her responsibilities

45.a) What are the Millennium development Goals (MDG)?

b) What is their current status in India?

c) Suggest ways to improve them. *2+3+5 (June 2014)*

CHAPTER

15

ANATOMY

BLOOD SUPPLY

1. Describe blood supply to female genital tract with help of well labelled diagram and explain the rationale of doing systematic devascularization. *4 (May 2024)*

2. Internal iliac artery. *5 (Oct 2023)*

3. a) Describe blood supply of reproductive organs. *5+5 (Dec 2022)*
   b) Role of uterine artery embolization in abnormal uterine bleeding.

4. a) Describe the course and branches of internal iliac artery. *4+6 (Aug 2021)*
   b) Discuss the indications and procedure of ligation of internal iliac artery.

5. Anatomy of internal iliac artery and its clinical significance in obstetrics and gynaecology. *5+5 (Dec 2019)*

6. a) Blood supply of female genital tract. *4+4+2 (June 2018)*
   b) What is the role of uterine artery embolization in obstetrics & gynaecology?
   c) Enumerate the complications associated with uterine artery embolization.

7. Discuss the blood supply, lymphatic drainage and nerve supply of cervix and its applied significance. *3+4+3 (Dec 2014)*

8. a) Vascular anatomy of anterior abdominal wall in relation to sites of port insertion. *3+ (3+4) (June 2016)*
   b) What are the entry related injuries in laparoscopy?

9. a) What are the major blood vessels supplying the pelvis? *4+4+2 (Dec 2013)*
   b) Discuss the clinical significance of collateral circulation of the pelvis with emphasis on internal iliac artery ligation?
   c) Enumerate the complications of internal iliac artery ligation?

LYMPHATIC SUPPLY

10. Lymphatic drainage of vulva. *5 (Oct 2023)*

11.a) Describe the lymphatic drainage of body of uterus. *4+6 (April 2023)*

b) Discuss the management of case of endometrial intraepithelial neoplasia in a 35 year old nulliparous woman.

12. Describe the lymphatic drainage of cervix with the help of labelled diagram.

13.a) Discuss the role of sentinel lymph node sampling in management of cervical cancer *4+6 (June 2022)*

b) Discuss the lymphatic drainage of female genital tract.

14.a) What is the role of lymphadenectomy in genital malignancies?

b) Write the branches of anterior and posterior divisions of internal iliac artery. *3+7 (Dec 2020)*

15. Describe briefly the procedure and indications of internal iliac. *5+5 (June 2020)*

16.a) Surgical anatomy and lymphatic drainage of cervix. *3+3+4 (Dec 2015)*

b) How can you preserve fertility in cervical cancer patient?

c) Basis of chemo-radiation and its application in a case of cancer cervix.

PELVIC ANATOMY

17.a) Write names of the muscles attached to the perineal body.

b) Course of pudendal nerve and its branches and supply in perineum. *2+4 (June 2025)*

18.a) With the help of diagram (s) describe the pelvic diaphragm.

b) Discuss the changes in pelvic floor during parturition.

c) How will you counsel a woman about Kegel's exercise? *4+3+3 (Oct 2024)*

19. De Lanceys level of pelvic supports. *5 (Oct 2023)*

20. With the help of diagrams, describe anatomy of perineum. *5 (Oct 2023)*

21.a) Describe with diagram Anal Sphincter Complex. *4+6 (Aug 2021)*

b) Discuss the classification, prevention and treatment of Obstetrical Anal Sphincter Injuries (OASIS).

22.a) Superficial perineal pouch. *5+5 (Dec 2019)*

b) Define course of pudendal nerve with reference to pudendal block.

23.a) Anatomy of perineum. *3+2+5 (June 2019)*

b) Classify obstetric anal sphincter injury.

c) Management of third degree perineal injury.

24.a) Anatomy of pelvic diaphragm. 5+5 (Dec 2018)
b) POP-Q classification of UV prolapse.

25.a) Embryological development of vagina with diagram. 3+2+5 (Dec 2018)
b) List various anatomical abnormalities causing primary anomalies.
c) Surgical management of congenital abnormality of Mullerian duct in primary amenorrhoea.

26.a) Surgical anatomy of pelvic organ support. 5+5 (June 2017)
b) Aetiology and surgical approach to nulliparous UV prolapse.

27.a) Significance of utero-sacral ligament in gynaecology. 5+5 (Dec 2016)
b) Anatomy of female perineum and its application in obstetrics?

28.a) Structural anatomy & function of anal sphincter complex.
b) Risk factors for anorectal injury during delivery and mention the changing concept of episiotomy. 4+ (3+3) (April 2016)

29.a) Various pelvic retroperitoneal spaces and their boundaries.
b) Importance of such spaces in gynaecology. 5+5 (June 2015)

30. Describe the supports of uterus and discuss posterior compartment defects. 6+4 (Dec 2014)

PELVIS

31.a) Describe the types of female pelvis. 5+5 (Dec 2022)
b) Discuss diagnosis and management of occipto-posterior presentation in anthropoid pelvis.

32.a) Describe the anatomical types of female pelvis. 3+7 (Dec 2020)
b) Discuss their obstetrical significance and impact on progress of labour.

URETER

33.a) Describe the anatomy of ureter in relation to female genital tract.
b) Enlist various sites of ureteral injury during obstetrics and gynaecological surgeries.
c) Describe the principles of surgery for prevention of ureteral injury during obstetrics and gynaecological surgeries. 3+3+4 (June 2022)

34.a) Describe course of ureter from origin till bladder insertion.
b) Discuss the sites where injury to ureter commonly occurs during surgery.
c) Discuss methods of preventing them. How will you manage accidental tying of ureter during suturing? 3+3+4 (June 2020)

35.a) Surgical anatomy of urinary bladder? 2+4+4 (June 2018)

b) How will you prevent bladder injury in obstetrics and gynaecology surgeries?

c) How will you identify bladder injury intra-operatively or postoperatively and manage it?

36.a) Course of ureter. 3+2 (2+3) (June 2015)

b) Where can it get injured or damaged during surgery in obstetrics and gynaecology.

c) Diagnosis of injury to the ureter and its management.

37.a) Describe the anatomy of pelvic ureter. 3+3+4 (Dec 2013)

b) What are the possible sites of ureteric injury during pelvic surgery?

c) How can these injuries be prevented?

ANTERIOR ABDOMINAL WALL

38.a) Describe anatomy of anterior abdominal wall. 5+5 (June 2018)

b) What are the different types of incisions used in gynaecological surgeries?

39.a) Vascular anatomy of anterior abdominal wall in relation to sites of port insertion. 3+ (3+4) (June 2016)

b) What are the entry related injuries in laparoscopy?

OTHERS

40.a) What are the anatomical features of placenta? 4+3+3 (June 2013)

b) Enumerate the development anomalies of placenta.

c) Describe the complications of morbidly adherent placenta.

CHAPTER

16

PHYSIOLOGY

FETAL CIRCULATION

1. a) Using appropriate diagram(s), describe fetal circulation.
   b) What changes occur in fetal circulation at birth?
   c) Discuss umbilical cord blood banking. *4+3+3 (Oct 2024)*
2. Foetal circulation with diaphragm. *5 (Dec 2018)*
3. Diagrammatic representation of foetal circulation. *5 (Dec 2016)*
4. Describe foetal circulation. *6 (Dec 2014)*

PLACENTA

5. a) Decidua – types, functions, diagram. *4+4+2 (June 2025)*
   b) Stages of trophoblast development.
   c) Trophoblastic invasion of spiral arteries & implications.
6. Describe the changes in the vascular architecture of uterus & endometrium in pregnancy. *4 (Oct 2024)*
7. a) Describe normal placentation. *5+5 (Dec 2022)*
   b) Discuss the impact of abnormal placentation.
8. Describe the placental circulation. *3 (June 2022)*
9. a) Explain details of implantation of pregnancy. *5+5 (June 2020)*
   b) What are the placental abnormalities associated with abnormal placentation?
10. a) Placental circulation. *5+5 (June 2019)*
    b) Placental circulatory disturbances.
11. Development of placenta. *5 (Dec 2018)*
12. a) What are hormones produced by placenta? *3+4+3 (April 2016)*
    b) What are the abnormalities of the placenta?
    c) What are the placental perfusion disorders?
13. Pathological evaluation of placenta. *5 (June 2015)*

14. Discuss different types of placental abnormalities and their significance. 6+4 (Dec 2014)

OVULATION

15.a) What is Corpus Luteum and its function? 5+5 (June 2021)
b) Discuss Corpus Luteum Dysfunction.

16.a) Physiology of ovulation 5+5 (Dec 2019)
b) Development of corpus luteum

17.a) Maturation of graffian follicle and ovulation. 3+2+5 (June 2019)
b) Significance of corpus luteum.
c) Diagnosis and management of corpus luteum deficiency.

18.a) Discuss the endocrinology of ovulation. 5+5 (June 2018)
b) Briefly discuss various modalities to assess ovulation.

19.a) Different phases of ovarian cycle. 3+3+4 (Dec 2015)
b) Process of development and differentiation of ovarian follicles.
c) Causes of ovulation.

20.a) What are the clinical indications of normal ovulatory function.
b) Enumerate the tests of ovulation.
c) Describe the basic principles of controlled ovarian hyperstimulation. 4+3+3 (June 2013)

21.a) Draw labelled diagram (s) of Graafian follicle. 3+4+3 (Dec 2011)
b) Describe the tests of ovarian reserve with critical interpretation of the results of each test.
c) Enumerate the treatment options for the women with poor ovarian reserve with other factors of fertility work up being normal.

LACTATION

22.a) Describe physiology of lactation. 5+5 (Oct 2023)
b) A-28-year-old para 1 lady reports with complaints of mastalgia, high grade fever and engorged breasts. Discuss management.

23.a) Describe the physiology of lactation. 5+5 (Dec 2022)
b) Discuss the management of a recently delivered mother with inability to initiate lactation.

24.a) Breast changes during pregnancy in primigravida. 4+6 (June 2019)

b) Common breast complications and its management in pregnancy and puerperium.

25.a) Describe the physiology of milk let down. *5+2+3 (Dec 2018)*
b) What is the early initiation of breastfeeding?
c) Steps to promote successful breastfeeding.

MENSTRUATION

26.a) Phases of menstrual cycle.
b) Hormonal regulation. *3+3 (June 2025)*

27.a) Physiological changes in vagina during menstrual cycle.
b) How will you diagnose a case of bacterial vaginosis?
c) What is syndromic approach in management of case with vaginal discharge? *2+4+4 (June 2018)*

SPERMATOGENESIS

28.a) What is the difference between Spermatogenesis & Spermiogenesis?
b) What changes occur in the sperm before fertilization? *2+2 (Oct 2024)*

AMNIOTIC FLUID

29. Describe physiology of amniotic fluid volume regulation. *4 (Dec 2022)*

30.a) Physiology of formation of amniotic fluid. *3+2+5 (Dec 2020)*
b) Functions of amniotic fluid.
c) Clinical implications of amniotic fluid abnormalities.

31. What is the physiological mechanism of formation of amniotic fluid? *3 (June 2013)*

PHYSIOLOGICAL CHANGES IN PREGNANCY

32.a) Describe physiological changes in coagulation during pregnancy.
b) Discuss the risk factors and methods to be considered for thrombo-pro-phylaxis in pregnancy. *2+8 (Dec 2022)*

33.a) Describe the haematological changes in pregnancy. *5+5 (Dec 2019)*
b) Correlate the haematological changes with physiological anaemia.

34. Discuss the renal physiology in pregnancy. *5 (June 2021)*

35. Changes in urinary tract in pregnancy. *3 (Dec 2020)*

36.a) What are different types of pathological changes in skin during pregnancy? *2+4+4 (June 2018)*

b) Enumerate the various causes of pruritus in pregnancy.

c) How will you manage a case of pregnancy related pruritus?

37.a) What are the physiological changes in thyroid function during pregnancy? *3+3+4 (June 2018)*

b) What are the complications associated with hypothyroidism during pregnancy?

c) How will you suspect and manage a case of post-partum thyroiditis?

38.a) What are the anatomical and physiological changes in hepato-biliary system in pregnancy? *5+5 (June 2018)*

b) Clinical and laboratory markers of intrahepatic cholestasis of pregnancy (IHC).

c) What are the foetal and neonatal morbidity of IHC and how will you prevent them?

39. a) Physiology of coagulation during pregnancy. *4+3+3 (Dec 2017)*

b) Mechanism of disseminated intravascular coagulation (DIC).

c) Blood transfusion and component therapy in DIC.

40.a) Physiological changes of thyroid gland in pregnancy. *4+3+3 (Dec 2015)*

b) Functions of foetal thyroid.

c) Role of routine screening for thyroid function in pregnancy.

HORMONES

41.a) Human chorionic gonadotropin (HCG) and its clinical relevance of its levels is early pregnancy. *6+4 (June 2018)*

b) Termination of missed abortion during first trimester.

42.a) What are the normal serum values of FSH, LH, E2, progesterone and testosterone? *5+5 (June 2016)*

b) What is the significance of monitoring them in gynaecology?

43.a) Functions of follicle stimulating hormone (FSH). *3+3+4 (Dec 2015)*

b) Indications for use of gonadotropins in gynaecology.

c) Commonly used anti-gonadotropins.

44.a) Describe the changes in serum beta Hcg levels in normal pregnancy.

b) Enumerate the indications for assessment of Beta Hcg levels in pregnancy and write their clinical significance. *4+ (2+4) (June 2014)*

45. What is the role of Inhibin A and B in obstetrics and gynaecology?

5+5 (June 2014)

OTHERS

46.a) How does wound healing occur? *5+5 (June 2020)*

b) What are the steps that can be taken to minimize the risk of dehiscence of a Caesarean scar?

CHAPTER

17

EMBRYOLOGY

1. Discuss the gonadal differentiation in male and female embryos. *4 (Oct 2024)*

2. With help of diagram (s), discuss embryology of female genital tract. *4 (Oct 2023)*

3. a) Describe the embryological development of the female reproductive tract in brief. *5+5 (June 2020)*
   b) Discuss diagnosis and management of bicornuate uterus.

4. a) Development of human embryo. *4+4+2 (June 2018)*
   b) What are the important aspects of sex differentiation during devel-op-ment?
   c) Enlist the teratogens that affect growing embryo.

5. a) Umbilical cord development and its structure. *4+6 (Dec 2015)*
   b) Enumerate various umbilical cord anomalies and their clinical impor-tance.

CHAPTER

18

DRUGS

PROGESTRONE

1. Critically evaluate WHO Medical eligibility criteria for injection medroxy progesterone acetate as a contraceptive? *10 (June 2021)*
2. Dinogest. *5 (Dec 2018)*
3. Role of progesterone in cases of recurrent pregnancy loss. *5 (June 2016)*
4. Evidence based use of progesterone in Obstetrics. *5 (June 2015)*
5. a) What are progestogens and how are they classified? *5+5 (Dec 2011)*
   b) Mention briefly the uses of progestogens in gynaecological practice?

SERM/ULIPRISTAL

6. Write a note on ulipristal acetate. *3 (Dec 2021)*
7. a) What are selective progesterone receptor modulators?
   b) What is the clinical utility of SERMS for the management of gynaecological conditions?
   c) Mifepristone. *2+5+3 (June 2020)*
8. a) Selective progesterone receptor modulator? *5+5 (Dec 2018)*
   b) Prediction of ovarian reserve?
9. Critically evaluate the role of ulipristal acetate for? *5+5 (June 2016)*
   a) Treatment of fibroids.
   b) Emergency contraception.
10. Selective oestrogen receptor modulator (SERM). *5 (June 2015)*

GNRH AGONISTS/ANTAGONISTS

11. a) What are GnRH agonists and antagonists? *6+4 (Dec 2019)*
    b) Discuss the clinical uses of GnRH agonists.
12. GnRH antagonists. *5 (Dec 2018)*
13. a) Functions of follicle stimulating hormone. *3+3+4 (Dec 2015)*

b) Indications for the use of gonadotropins in gynaecology?

c) Commonly used anti-gonadotropins.

DRUGS IN PREGNANCY

14.a) Describe various antihypertensive drugs in pregnancy including dosage and side effects of each. *6+4 (June 2022)*

b) Describe postpartum antihypertensive drug of choice in a lactating mother.

15.a) FDA for the drugs used in pregnancy. *2+4+4 (June 2019)*

b) Maternal and foetal side effects of antibacterial antibiotics.

c) Pregnancy associated physiological changes and their potential influences on antimicrobial pharmacokinetics.

16. Low molecular weight heparin and its uses in obstetrics. *5 (June 2015)*

TOCOLYTICS

17. Role of Atosiban as a tocolytic agent. *5 (June 2017)*

18.a) What are the indications and contraindications of tocolysis?

b) Enumerate the agents available and write their doses and side effects. *4+6 (June 2014)*

CORTICOSTEROIDS

19. Describe the various drug, dosage and recommendations of antenatal corticosteroid therapy. *5 (June 2022)*

OTHERS

20.a) What are inositols? *3+ (3+4) (June 2016)*

b) Physiological role and clinical utility of inositols in PCOD.

21. Neuroprotector role of antepartum magnesium sulphate. *5 (June 2016)*

22.a) Describe the physiology of oxytocin in pregnancy. *3+2+5 (June 2014)*

b) What is the pharmacokinetics and therapeutic role of oxytocin in labour?

23.a) Discuss the pharmacodynamics of misoprostol. *2+3+5 (Dec 2013)*

b) Enumerate the indications for the use of misoprostol in obstetrics.

c) How will you monitor a primi-gravida who has been induced at full term with vaginal misoprostol?

CHAPTER

19

MISCELLENEOUS

STEM CELL BANKING

1. a) Describe the various indications of umbilical cord sampling of newborn at delivery. *5+5 (May 2024)*
   b) Discuss the role and procedure of umbilical cord blood banking as a biological insurance.

2. Role of stem cell therapy. *5 (April 2023)*

3. a) What are stem cells? *2+8 (June 2020)*
   b) Role of stem cell therapy in Obstetrics and gynaecology.

4. a) What are stem cells? *2+8 (June 2020)*
   b) Role of stem cell therapy in obstetrics and gynaecology.

5. a) What are stem cells? *4+6 (June 2019)*
   b) Role of stem cell therapy in gynaecology.

6. Write short notes on: *5+5 (Dec 2013)*
   a) Complications of blood transfusion
   b) Stem cell banking

SEXUAL ACT

7. a) Principles of forensic evidence in a victim of sexual assault.
   b) POCSO Act.
   c) Counselling of the survivor of sexual assault. *3+4+3 (Dec 2020)*

8. Examination of a victim of sexual assault. *5 (Dec 2016)*

9. a) What are the basic principles of forensic evidence collection in a sexual assault survivor? *4+3+3 (June 2016)*
   b) How will you counsel a women subjected to sexual assault?
   c) Post exposure prophylaxis against STI/RTI in such cases.

10. What is the impact of domestic violence on sexual and reproductive health? *4+6 (June 2014)*

11. a) What are the basic principles of forensic evidence collection in a victim of sexual assault? *4+3+3 (June 2013)*
    b) Describe counselling of a woman subjected to sexual assault.
    c) Describe briefly post exposure prophylaxis against HIV.

12. a) Enumerate the key points in setting adolescent health clinic in your hospital.
    b) What are the reproductive health hazards of adolescent girls?
    c) Describe preventive strategies to reduce reproductive health hazards in adolescent girls through the clinic. *3+3+4 (June 2013)*

HDU/ICU

13. a) Briefly discuss the WHO labour care guide. *5+5 (Oct 2023)*
    b) Enumerate admission criteria for equipped obstetric ICU.

14. a) Principles of obstetric high dependency unit (HDU)? *5+5 (June 2016)*
    b) How will you set up HDU in your hospital?

OTHERS

15. a) Describe various abdominal incisions used for gynaecology surgeries.
    b) Briefly discuss physiology of wound healing.
    c) Enumerate steps that can be taken to reduce surgical site infections. *4+4+2 (Oct 2023)*

16. Immunisation during pregnancy. *5 (April 2023)*

17. Discuss role of Laser in Gynaecology. *5 (Dec 2021)*

18. a) What are the indications of massive blood transfusion? *4+6 (June 2021)*
    b) Discuss the protocols and adverse reactions of massive blood transfusion in Obstetrics.

19. a) Teratogens in pregnancy. *5+5 (Dec 2019)*
    b) Elucidate the viral teratogens.

20. a) Immune adaptations of pregnancy. *4+6 (June 2019)*
    b) Maternal immunisation for different pathogens.

21. a) Pathophysiology of obesity. *4+6 (June 2019)*
    b) Effect of obesity in reproductive life of women.

22. a) Foetal inflammatory response syndrome (FIRS) and its morbidity.
    b) Sudden intra-partum foetal demise: causes and counselling. *5+5 (June 2017)*

23.a) What are the risks of pregnancy at advanced maternal age?
b) How will you screen and manage such a patient? *3+ (3+4) (June 2014)*

24.a) Risk factors for hospital acquired infections (HAI) and enumerate its causative organisms. *(3+2)+3+2 (Dec 2016)*
b) Clinical picture of common HAI in obstetrics and gynaecology.
c) Prevention of HAI.

25.a) How do you calculate BMI? *1+3+6 (June 2016)*
b) What are the different ranges of BMI?
c) What is its relevance in obstetrics & gynaecology?

26.a) How is fluid and electrolyte balance maintained in the post-operative period? *3+ (3+4) (June 2016)*
b) How would you diagnose and manage post-operative fluid and electrolyte imbalance?

27. Necrotising fasciitis. *5 (Dec 2015)*

28.a) What are the biochemical markers of bone turnover? *4+3+3 (June 2014)*
b) How is bone mineral density evaluated?
c) What are therapeutic options for osteoporosis?

29.a) What are micronutrients? *4+3 (Dec 2011)*
b) Describe the role of four micronutrients in maternal and foetal well-being.
c) What are the indications and modes of paternal iron therapy in pregnancy?

CHAPTER

20

GENETICS

NIPT

1. Three situations where NIPS cannot be offered. *3 (June 2025)*

2. a) What is NIPT?
   b) What is the current role of NIPT? *5+5 (Dec 2019)*

3. a) What is cell free foetal DNA? *5+5 (June 2018)*
   b) Discuss the role of cell free foetal DNA screening in obstetrical practice

4. a) NIPT. *5 (Dec 2018)*

5. NIPT (Non-invasive prenatal testing. *5 (Dec 2016)*

6. Foetal cell free DNA in maternal blood. *5 (June 2016)*

7. a) Cell free foetal DNA screening and its indications. *(2+2)+3+3(June 2015)*
   b) Invasive tests for prenatal diagnosis and their uses.

PGT (PREIMPLANTATION GENETIC TESTING)

8. What is preimplantation genetic testing? *5 (April 2023)*

9. a) What is preimplantation genetic testing and different techniques used for it? *5+5 (Dec 2020)*
   b) Clinical applications of preimplantation genetic testing.

10. Role of preimplantation diagnostic technique. *5 (June 2020)*

11. a) What is pre-implantation genetic diagnosis (PGD)? *1+(3+3+2) (June 2016)*
    b) What is comprehensive chromosomal screening (CCS)?
    c) What are the indications, benefits and risk of PGD & CCS?

12. Pre-implantation genetic diagnosis. *5 (Dec 2014)*

DOWN'S SYNDROME

13. a) What is Down syndrome? *5+5 (Dec 2019)*
    b) Describe the different screening methods for Down syndrome in pregnancy.

14. Biochemical screening for Down's syndrome. *5 (June 2017)*

15.a) What are the risk factors for neural tube defect? *4+3+3 (April 2016)*
b) Screening for Down's syndrome.
c) What are the pre-implantation genetic testings available?

16.a) Trimester-wise antenatal tests to be offered to a pregnant woman with a previous child having Down's syndrome. *5+5 (Dec 2018)*
b) Antenatal monitoring of monochorionic twin pregnancy.

GENETIC COUNSELLING

17.a) Carrier screening for genetic disorders.
b) Diagnostic genetic tests & utility.
c) Screening twins/higher-order for aneuploidy.

18.a) What is pre-conceptional counselling? *5+5 (Dec 2020)*
b) How will you counsel a young woman pre-conceptionally with history of previous baby with thalassemia major?

19. Gene Xpert. *5 (Dec 2018)*

20.a) Pre-conceptional counselling. *3+ (3+4) (June 2015)*
b) A patient with previous history of neural tube defect in a child comes to ask about chances of similar defect in her next pregnancy. How will you counsel and manage her next pregnancy?

21.a) What is genetic counselling? *2+4+4 (Dec 2015)*
b) When and to whom should we offer prenatal genetic counselling?
c) What is pre-implantation genetic diagnosis?

22.a) What is genetic counselling? *2+3+5 (June 2014)*
b) In which patients is it required?
c) What are the procedures that can be performed to aid diagnosis?

23. Discuss the uses and recommendations for umbilical cord banking. *5 (June 2022)*

OTHERS

24.a) Strategies for aneuploidy screening. *4+3 (June 2025)*
b) Screening for pre-eclampsia in 1st trimester.

25.a) What is chromosome microarray analysis? *5+5 (Dec 2020)*
b) What is the clinical application of chromosome microarray analysis?

26.a) Characteristics of a good screening test. *5+5 (June 2015)*
b) Screening protocols for aneuploidies.

CHAPTER

21

FETAL MEDICINE

FETAL MEDICINE PROCEDURES

1. Enumerate indications, procedure and complications of fetal reduction treatment. *4 (Oct 2023)*

2. Discuss intrauterine fetal blood transfusion. *5 (Oct 2023)*

3. Fetoscopic surgery. *5 (Oct 2023)*

4. a) Amniocentesis. *5+5 (April 2023)*
   b) Intrauterine transfusion.

5. Discuss the staging of twin-twin transfusion syndrome and management options. *5 (April 2023)*

6. a) Describe various in-utero intrafetal therapy - indications and procedures.
   b) Enlist various complications related to in-utero intrafetal therapy.
   c) What is meant by Ex-utero Intrafetal Treatment procedure (EXIT)? *4+4+2 (June 2022)*

7. a) Define foetal therapy. *2+8 (June 2021)*
   b) Discuss the principles, indications and categorization of foetal therapy.

8. a) What are the different methods of foetal therapy?
   b) Describe EXIT surgery. *7+3 (Dec 2020)*

9. a) Define foetal blood sampling and enumerate its indications.
   b) Sites and complications of FBS. *4+6 (June 2020)*

10. a) What is chorionic villus sampling and how it is done? *5+5 (Dec 2019)*
    b) Clinical applications of chorionic villus sampling.

11. a) What are the different methods of foetal therapy? *7+3 (Dec 2019)*
    b) Describe EXIT surgery.

12. a) What are the indications of chronic villous sampling? *4+2+4 (Dec 2012)*
    b) When is it performed?
    c) What are its complications and how do you manage them?

13. a) What are the genetic indications of amniocentesis? *4+2+4 (Dec 2012)*

b) When should it be performed?

c) Discuss its complications and their prevention.

OBSTETRIC USG

14. What are safety guidelines for imaging modalities in pregnancy? *3 (Dec 2021)*

15.a) What are the different methods to assess the chorionicity in pregnancy?

b) What are the implications of chorionicity in management of twin pregnancy? *5+5 (June 2020)*

16.a) What are the components of a standard ultrasound examination in the 1st & 2nd trimester? *4+4+2 (April 2016)*

b) What are the guidelines for Nuchal thickness?

c) What are abnormalities in measuring the biparietal diameter?

17. a) What are the foetal anatomical parameters to be evaluated in a second trimester foetal anomaly detection scan. *3+3+4 (Dec 2015)*

b) Enumerate neural tube defects of foetus.

c) How will you manage subsequent pregnancy with prior history of neural tube defect foetus?

18. Role of USG in the management of mono-chorionic twin pregnancy. *5 (Dec 2015)*

19. Clinical importance of yolk sac within the gestational sac in obstetrics. *5 (Dec 2015)*

20. Sonography in first trimester. *5 (June 2015)*

21. Discuss soft markers for foetal aneuploidy. *10 (Dec 2014)*

OBSTETRIC DOPPLER

22. Discuss role of colour Doppler in modern day obstetrics. *5 (Oct 2023)*

23.a) What is the role of Doppler velocimetry in assessment of placental circulation?

b) Outline its clinical application in pregnancy. *3+4 (June 2022)*

24. Uterine artery Doppler studies in pregnancy. *5 (April 2016)*

25.a) Clinical importance of Doppler studies in foetal growth restriction.

b) What are the perinatal complications in such a case? Outline their management. *5+5 (Dec 2016)*

26.a) What are the principles of foetal ductus venosus flow assessment?
b) What are the normal and abnormal waveforms?
c) What are the indications for its use?
d) How does it modify obstetric management? *3+2+2+3 (Dec 2016)*

27. What is Doppler flow velocimetry and its importance in pregnancy? *4+6 (Dec 2015)*

28.a) What do you understand by MCA-PSV? *4+6 (Dec 2014)*
b) Discuss its role in obstetrics.

29. Briefly discuss the clinical importance of Doppler studies in Obstetrics. *4 (Dec 2014)*

30.a) Discuss in brief the principles of Doppler velocimetry.
b) Enumerate the vessels studied during pregnancy and their impact on pregnancy management. *2+ (3+5) (June 2014)*

31. Describe the utility of Doppler studies in:
a) Multiple gestation *3+4+3 (June 2012)*
b) Infertile women
c) Placenta previa

FETAL ANOMALIES

32. Ventriculomegaly in fetus - causes and management. *5 (April 2023)*

33. Discuss non-invasive techniques for prenatal diagnosis for foetal anomalies. *7 (Dec 2022)*

34. Cystic hygroma in foetus during anomaly scan. *5 (June 2020)*

35. A foetus primi-gravida at 19 weeks of gestation is noticed to have liver calcification on ultrasound. *5+5 (June 2018)*
a) Discuss the causes of foetal liver calcification.
b) How will you manage this case?

36. A primigravida conceived with in-vitro fertilization after long term infertility reported at 24 weeks gestation with bilateral renal pelvicalyceal dilatation in fetus. *5+5 (June 2018)*
a) Discuss the causes.
b) How will you manage this case?

37.a) Biochemical markers used for the diagnosis of fetal anomalies in the first trimester. *5+5 (Dec 2016)*
b) Diagnosis of congenital diaphragmatic hernia during pregnancy.

38. Presence of echogenic bowel in antenatal ultrasonography. *5 (June 2016)*

DOWNS SYNDROME

39.a) How can sonography augment aneuploidy screening? *6+4 (Dec 2020)*

b) Enumerate the soft signs associated with foetal trisomy.

40.a) Guidelines for Nuchal translucency measurement in first trimester fetal anomaly screening. *5+5 (Dec 2016)*

b) Standard examination of foetal anatomy in an anomaly scan at second trimester.

FETAL MRI

41. Foetal MRI: indications and role. *5 (June 2017)*

PCPNDT ACT

42. What is PCPNDT Act? *2 (June 2019)*

43. PCPNDT Act for the obstetrician. *5 (Dec 2016)*

CHAPTER

22

RADIOLOGY

GYNEC USG

1. Differentiate arcuate, septate, bicorporeal uterus on 3D USG (with diagrams). *5 (June 2025)*
2. Role of interventional radiology in Obstetrics and Gynaecology. *5 (Oct 2023)*
3. a) Discuss the advances in imaging modalities for gynaecologic malignancies. *5+5 (April 2023)*
   b) HIFU.
4. Role of uterine artery embolization in abnormal uterine bleeding. *5 (Dec 2022)*
5. Role of interventional radiology in gynaecology. *5 (April 2016)*
6. Role of imaging in adenomyosis. *5 (June 2020)*
7. Describe the Doppler principle. Write about the use of Doppler studies in Gynaecological cases. *5+5 (June 2020)*
8. Role of TVS in the investigation and management of infertility. *5 (June 2017)*
9. Role of ultrasonography in infertility. *5 (Dec 2016)*

MRI

10. MRI in obstetrics. *10 (Dec 2019)*
11. Indications of MRI in obstetrics. *5+5 (Dec 2015)*
12. Role of MRI in obstetrics and gynaecology. *5+5 (June 2015)*

PET CT

13. Role of PET-CT in gynaecology. *5 (Dec 2020)*

CHAPTER

23

ENDOSCOPY

1. Modern uses of endoscopy in Gynecology. *5 (Oct 2023)*

2. a) Ergonomics in endoscopic surgery. *5+5 (Dec 2018)*
   b) Principles of use of electro-surgical unit in gynaecological surgery.

3. Natural Orifice Transluminal Endoscopic Surgery in Obstetrics and Gynaecology. *10 (Dec 2022)*

4. a) What are the principles underlying the use of electrosurgical energy in operative procedures? *3+3+4 (June 2012)*
   b) Critically evaluate the use of monopolar versus bipolar diathermy.
   c) Describe the indications, methodology and complications of ovarian drilling in cases of polycystic ovarian syndrome.

HYSTEROSCOPY

5. a) Tools for hysteroscopic septum resection. *4+4+2 (June 2025)*
   b) Media used with different energy sources.
   c) Preventing water intoxication.

6. a) Discuss role of hysteroscopy in modern day ART practice.
   b) Discuss pros and cons of the distension media used in hysteroscopy. *5+5 (Oct 2023)*

7. a) Role of hysteroscopy in gynaecological conditions. *4+2+4 (Dec 2016)*
   b) Complications of hysteroscopy.
   c) Preventive steps one should take to avoid complications of hysteroscopy.

8. a) What is office hysteroscopy? *1+5+4 (Dec 2016)*
   b) What are its indications, prerequisites and precautions?
   c) Management of endometrial polyps on hysteroscopy.

9. Role of hysteroscopy in the management of infertility. *5 (Dec 2015)*

10. a) Enumerate indications and complications of hysteroscopy.
    b) How will you manage complications of hysteroscopy? *(3+3)+4 (June 2014)*

11. a) What are the etiological factors causing intrauterine adhesions?

b) What are its clinical consequences?

c) Describe the hysteroscopic management of intrauterine adhesions and prevention of its recurrence? *3+3+4 (June 2013)*

LAPAROSCOPY

12. Perioperative complications of electro-surgery in laparoscopic surgeries and their prevention? *5 (June 2017)*

13.a) Role of laparoscopy in gynaecology. *3+4+3 (Dec 2015)*

b) Evaluate the energy sources used for haemostasis in endoscopic surgery.

c) Advantages of robotic surgery.

14.a) Indications and complications of laparoscopic surgery. *5+5 (June 2015)*

b) How is robotic surgery different from laparoscopic surgery and its role in gynaecology?

15.a) What is the preoperative preparation for laparoscopic surgery?

b) What are the indications and complications of laparoscopic surgery in Gynaecology?

c) How can these complications be prevented? *2+ (3+3) +2 (Dec 2013)*

16.a) What are the indications of operative laparoscopy? *3+4+3 (Dec 2012)*

b) What are the complications of operative laparoscopy?

c) How can they be anticipated and prevented?

ROBOTICS

17. Robotic surgery in gynaecology. *5 (June 2016)*

CHAPTER

24

PROCEDURES

1. Discuss indications, procedure and complications of Uterine artery embolization. *10 (June 2021)*

2. Third generation of endometrial ablation techniques. *5+5 (Dec 2018)*

3. Thermal endometrial ablation versus levonorgestrel IUS in management of menorrhagia. *5 (June 2017)*

4. Different interventional modalities in management of benign gynaecological diseases. *5 (April 2016)*

5. Uterine artery embolization. *5 (June 2015)*

6. a) What is uterine artery embolization? *3+3+4 (June 2013)*
   b) Enumerate its indications in contemporary obstetrics and gynaecological practice.
   c) Describe its techniques, advantages and disadvantages in brief.

CHAPTER

25

GYNEC SURGERIES

1. a) Ergonomics of TLH port positions. *5+5 (June 2025)*
   b) Complications of TLH.

2. Uterus transplant: indications and future prospective. *5 (June 2022)*

3. a) What are the ethical issues involved with uterine transplantation?
   b) Patient selection, evaluation and screening for uterine transplantation. *3+7 (Dec 2020)*

4. a) How do you avoid ureteric injuries in endoscopic surgery?
   b) Management of ureterovaginal fistula after hysterectomy. *5+5 (June 2020)*

5. Evaluate TLH (total laparoscopic hysterectomy) vs. NDVH (non-descent vaginal hysterectomy). *5 (Dec 2016)*

6. Uterine transplant: Indications, procedure, ethical considerations and cause of failure of uterine transplant. *2+3+2+3 (June 2016)*

7. a) Classify and describe briefly the types of hysterectomy.
   b) Which are the cases where ureteric damage is more likely and how can it be prevented? *4+3+3 (June 2014)*

8. a) What is non descent vaginal hysterectomy? *2+3+2+3 (June 2013)*
   b) What are its indications and pre-requisites?
   c) Enumerate its immediate and late post-operative complications.
   d) Describe its advantages and disadvantages in comparison to laparoscopic hysterectomy.